Guidance and Control of Spacecraft

Edward Hymoff

Coordinating Editor:
James V. Bernardo, Director
Educational Programs and Services
National Aeronautics and Space Administration

 Holt, Rinehart and Winston, Inc., New York

Edward Hymoff was born in Boston, Massachusetts. He received a BS degree from Boston University and an MA from the Russian Institute at Columbia University.

In 1958 he spent six months behind the iron curtain, including two months in the Soviet Union, on a series of writing assignments which included interviews with top Soviet space scientists.

An active pilot, Mr. Hymoff specializes in aerospace and military writing. He is an active member in several professional societies including the Aviation Writers Association, American Institute of Aeronautics and Astronautics, and the National Press Club.

He is the author of *The Desert Air War*, co-author of *The Mission*, a book about President Lyndon Johnson's World War II exploits, and more than 1000 magazine articles. Mr. Hymoff is a recent winner of The Aviation/Space Writers 1956 Writing Award in the category of nonfiction books. *The Mission* was selected by the Writing Awards Committee as an "outstanding example of excellence in writing."

Original drawings: Versatron Corporation

Preface

Ever since man evolved into a creature of curiosity, he has expressed a desire to travel—to go somewhere, anywhere.

Now, twentieth-century man stands on the threshold of space. Where he goes in space is a question that can only be answered by the future, for the universe as we know it is limitless. For man today, space is a hostile environment, just as our world was hostile to our ancestors during their peregrinations across the deserts, the mountains, and the smaller seas.

Somehow or other, man has developed various methods of guiding himself to his many destinations. These "guidance systems" have been both biological and mechanical. The evolution of "guidance systems" has permitted man to evolve from caveman to the physical specimens which we now call "pilot," "astronaut," and "cosmonaut."

It stands to reason that a book about the guidance and control of spacecraft must begin at the beginning with early man, the creature who has evolved into the twentieth-century man of the Space Age. Man historically has conquered space as he knew it then and knows it now—the oceans, the deserts, the plains, the mountains, the sky above, and the sea. All this, too, is space.

In order to traverse "space" on the earth's surface, beneath the sea and in the sky above, man has built spacecraft that have taken the form of wheeled carts, rafts, and boats powered by oars and sail, balloons, sailplanes, mechanically-powered aircraft, powered-wheeled vehicles, and ships and submarines —and, finally, man-carrying rockets. Even man himself is a spacecraft—a body housing a brain or "guidance system"— who throughout his history has found the means to go from one place to another and reach his goal. Man was—and still is —the guidance system. What he has developed to assist him in reaching his destination is the product of his imagination and genius.

He has learned to guide himself on journeys utilizing landmarks, the sun, the moon, and the stars, and by developing other tools that we now refer to as navigational aids—the sextant and the gyroscope.

With the advent of the Space Age on October 4, 1957, when the first man-made object to orbit the earth was successfully launched, the word "sputnik" was added to our lexicon and a host of questions faced modern scientists. Among them were problems of how to send a vehicle into space and bring it back to earth, and how to send it to the moon and return.

These problems pose the question of how to guide and control spacecraft. To understand the problems, we naturally had to begin at the beginning.

In writing this book, I am indebted greatly to aerospace author Martin Caidin for the use of his massive reference library on the subject of space flight; Mr. Ken Brigham of The Sperry Gyroscope Company; Mr. James Porterfield and Mr. Forler Massnick of the Honeywell Corporation and Carl Byoir and Associates; Dr. Taft Russell, President, Applied Electronics Corp. of New Jersey; Mr. Bernard Pokat for his expert advice on nautical navigation, and my many friends at NASA who are now making possible a flight to the moon and back.

Contents

To Kurt

1

Guidance Used by Primitive Man

Tens of thousands of years ago our ancestors began out of curiosity to wander from their caves to find out for themselves if the grass was greener in the next valley. Primitive man used his superior intelligence to mark his progress with a sign, with a smaller rock placed atop a larger one; a "blaze" mark on a tree by stripping off bark, or a sign scratched on the ground.

Whatever means of communication that existed between primitive men, there was the addition of the "sign"—the first written word, so to speak. The first signs were used to guide man back to his cave and later his village. As he began to wander afar on journeys that lasted days instead of hours, he focused his attention on natural landmarks—trees, hills, cliffs, rock projections and mountains. By keeping these various landmarks in sight, he could always find his way back to his people.

When he first took to the water in rafts and crude boats, the rivers automatically guided him back and forth to his destinations. When he first went to sea, always making sure to stay within sight of land, he focused his attention on a particular landmark which guided him home.

Primitive tribes soon expanded into nations, and man progressed to the point where he began travelling distances measured in hundreds and then thousands of miles. The first caravans were guided by the sun, the moon, and the star patterns, or constellations. In the northern hemisphere, the North Star—the star Polaris or Pole Star—became the guiding star for travellers who mapped out the heavens at the same time they began mapping what they knew of the earth.

Man was, for all practical purposes, the first "black box" or guidance system. Using his eyes, ears, sense of smell and

Fig. 1-1.   Primitive man used landmarks to guide himself to his cave dwelling.

touch, and his voice—all coordinated by his intelligence—he slowly but surely built the sub-systems that helped him move about. His first boat may have been the trunk of a tree floating on a lake or river. With a pole he learned to guide this log in various directions. Later he utilized wood to build boats and devised an oar which, when turned in the water to force the flow against a flat surface, moved the boat in a controlled direction. This was man's first application of hydrodynamics, a principle later utilized in the study of flight. Still later the wind was caught in a sail, and power other than the pole and oar propelled and guided boats. Although the words "guidance," and "control" were not part of man's early language, he continued to use and improve on methods to help get him to his destinations.

The early sign used by primitive man later evolved into maps, drawings of the areas with which man was most familiar. They were pictures of the ground, showing its shape, location and types of trails, landmarks, woods, swamps, rivers, lakes, hills, mountains and shorelines. These early maps gave man two views of the areas through which he wanted to travel. There was a ground level view and the view from directly overhead, or how man imagined what the earth should look like if he were a bird.

Until the advent of the compass, man used a process of dead reckoning which, later in the age of flight was called "seat of the pants flying." For centuries, mariners used dead reckoning to navigate their ships when out of sight of land, and during bad weather. This method of travel meant that the sun, the moon and the stars were used to guide a vessel in the proper direction until the next landmark was sighted.

Time then became a factor in control and guidance. Man first began to tell time by noting the positions of shadows made by trees and rocks. He determined that when the shadow of some familiar object reached a certain point, he had just enough time left to get back to his cave, his village or his tribe before dark. He knew he could travel only during the daylight hours. The ability to tell time also helped him to understand that when the sun was rising or setting, it marked a direction which he could use for guidance.

When he built his first timekeeping device by simply sticking a stick in the ground and using its shadow as a sun-dial. This shadow gave him a sense of direction.

From the dawn of history, when life first appeared on earth, the senses of living organisms guided them through their development. Animals and man used their senses to move about and return to their havens. Thus the brain became the first guidance system and today is basic in every living creature that has the ability to move from one place to another.

Thousands of years passed after man discovered that the heavens afforded a method of navigation, before the compass made its appearance as a device for determining direction. Consisting of a small bar magnet or a magnetized needle attached to a pointer, the compass was mounted to rotate freely in a horizontal plane. The compass needle aligns itself with the Earth's magnetic field, and a scale marked in degrees is used to specify directions relative to this magnetic field. The first magnetic compasses made their appearance about 700 years ago, employing a piece of lodestone or magnetite delicately balanced on a piece of carved wood.

The compass was followed by the first sextant, developed some 400 years ago, to measure the altitude of celestial objects by determining the angular distance above the horizon. This angular distance, which varies with location and the seasons, was utilized by early explorers in the Seventeenth Century to determine the locations of their vessels on long journeys into the great unknown.

The development of intelligence over the centuries and man's ability to guide himself across the far reaches of the earth and navigate the oceans led to the discovery of new and strange continents.

2

Early Flight Guidance

The early dream of our ancestors was to travel to unknown places on earth—and to fly. As early as 300 years before Christ, the Chinese started sending military signals by kite. They and the Greeks even hoisted themselves a few rough-and-tumble feet off the ground by kite.

But flight evaded our ancestors. Overhead, birds lifted—darting, soaring, gliding and hovering in the fully articulated flight which man at that time had been unable to duplicate. He tried jumping from towers. Straining strange sinews, he plummeted to oblivion—futilely fluttering the artificial wings and tails he strapped to his body.

In the Thirteenth Century, Oxford philosopher Roger Bacon, followed three centuries later by Leonardo da Vinci, wrote about wing-flapping vehicles (ornithopters) designed to enable man to fly like a bird; but no ornithopter has ever been successful. Da Vinci also sketched parachute and rotary-wing designs. However, man first had to float on his magic sea of air. He pondered the buoyant, level flight of clouds and wondered why smoke and sparks rose. Francesco de Lana, an Italian Jesuit, proposed an aerial boat suspended from four paper-thin copper globes 20 feet in diameter which would be controlled and guided by pumping out air before take-off and letting it back into the globes for descent. De Lana didn't realize that atmospheric pressure would have crushed the vacuum "balloons" he proposed; and he doubted that God would let his craft fly "since it would cause much disturbance among the civil and political governments of mankind."

It took another 113 years before the Montgolfier brothers in France finally in 1783 flew a balloon filled with smoke and heated air from burning charcoal. Three months later, King

Louis XVI of France watched while the first living beings ascended—a duck, a rooster and a sheep. With the success of that flight, the King offered a criminal sentenced to death the honor of becoming the first man to "fly." But the King's historian, Jean François Pilatre de Rozier, asked that he be permitted to make "man's first flight." He did, on October 15, 1783, only to become the first airman fatality two years later, falling 3,000 feet to his death when the balloon he was flying in suddenly lost its lifting ability.

In 1793, the French Government formed an air arm, and the revolutionary army began sending up a tethered balloon for reconnaissance. One with a two-man crew was put aloft at Manberg, under siege by Dutch and Austrian forces. The Austrians, fearing their every move was being watched, lifted the siege and the French then whisked the balloon off to Charleroi where a French offensive was under way. When it popped up there, the enemy garrison reportedly was frightened into immediate surrender.

Early balloons and those that followed were all tethered to the ground. If they were permitted to fly at the whim of the wind, there was no method of controlling or guiding them to any definite destination. Napoleon disbanded the balloon corps at the turn of the century, and it wasn't until the War of 1812 that the Prussians began to use observation balloons against the French. Later, during the siege of Venice in 1849, the first free balloons were utilized for military purposes. Carefully gauging the direction of the wind, the Austrians sent unmanned small hot-air balloons guided by air currents over the city. Each carried a 30-pound bomb with a time fuse, but they did little damage.

In 1852, a giant step forward was taken in the guidance and control of spacecraft when Henri Guifford, a French engineer, propelled his cigar-shaped balloon through the air with an engine. Its three-horsepower steam engine turning a screw or propeller sped this flying machine a distance of 17 miles at five miles an hour.

Man had finally conquered the sky.

It remained for rigid aircraft to prove finally that heavier-than-air vehicles also could conquer the sky. The first biplane glider was built in England in 1810 by Sir George Cayley. It could fly on the currents of air, but there was no way of controlling its direction of flight. A few years later, Sir George built a larger flying machine and sent his coachman on an uncontrolled flight for 900 feet. The glider crashed, without injuring the frightened coachman who immediately quit his job. Cayley quit building gliders.

It was left for the Wright brothers, in December 1903, to build the first true heavier-than-air flying machine powered by a gasoline engine, with a man at the controls to guide it along a predetermined course. Six years later Louis Bleriot piloted an airplane from France to England, spanning the English Channel and landing exactly where he wanted to.

Controlled flight had arrived.

Controlled flight is based on similar scientific principles or laws, whether this flight be in the air, in space, or in the sea. No matter what type of "flight" is involved, these forces act and react in all manner of vehicles suspended and in motion, whether we call them aircraft, spacecraft or submarine.

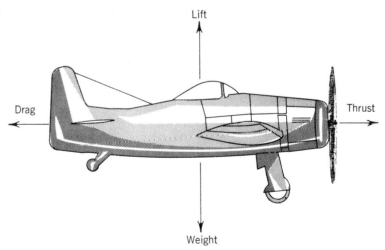

Fig. 2-1.   Forces acting on aircraft in level flight.

Four forces react on vehicles in level flight—*lift*, the upward-acting force; *weight*, or gravity, the downward-acting force; *thrust*, the forward-acting force; and *drag*, the backward-acting, or retarding force of inertia and resistance. Lift opposes weight and thrust opposes drag.

Although these forces extend to submarines and spacecraft, which we will discuss later, they apply to the guidance and control of aircraft. Drag and weight are forces inherent in anything lifted from the earth and moved through the air. Thrust and lift are artificially-created forces used to overcome the forces of nature and enable an airplane to fly. The engine propeller combination is designed to produce thrust to overcome drag. The wing is designed to produce lift to overcome the weight or pull of gravity.

To understand how lift is produced, we must examine the phenomenon discovered many years ago by the scientist Bernoulli and later called Bernoulli's Principle: *The pressure of a fluid (liquid or gas) decreases at points where the speed of the fluid increases.* In other words, Bernoulli found that within the same fluid, in this case air, high speed or flow is associated with low pressure, and low speed with high pressure. This principle was first used to explain changes in the pressure of fluid flowing within a pipe whose cross-sectional area varied. In the wide section of the gradually-narrowing pipe, the fluid moves at low speed, producing high pressure. As the pipe narrows it must contain the same amount of fluid. In this narrow section, the fluid moves at high speed, producing low pressure—or lift.

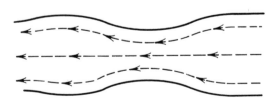

Fig. 2-2.   Flow of air through a Venturi tube.

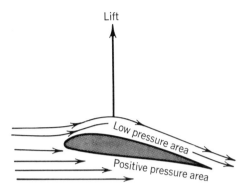

Fig. 2-3.   Difference in pressure between upper and lower wing surfaces produce lift.

An important application of this phenomenon is the lift given to the wing of an airplane, an airfoil. The airfoil—also used to guide and control the aircraft—is designed to *increase the velocity of the airflow above* its surface, thereby *decreasing pressure above* the airfoil. Simultaneously, the impact of the air on the lower surface of the airfoil increases the pressure below. This combination of pressure decrease above and increase below produces lift.

You have probably held your flattened hand out of the window of a moving automobile. As you inclined your hand to the wind, the force of air pushed against it forcing your hand to rise. The airfoil (in this case your hand) was deflecting the wind, which in turn created an equal and opposite dynamic pressure on the lower surface of the airfoil, forcing it up and back. The upward component of this force is lift; the backward component is drag.

Although these physical laws governing the flight of heavier-than-air craft were little known prior to the birth of the airplane at the turn of the century, early aviation pioneers quickly learned what forces affected the flying machine and how to compensate with design, so that the airplane could be controlled and guided to its destination. They discovered that an aircraft in flight turns about three axes and that any vehicle in flight operates on this principle, as we shall see later.

Whenever the attitude of the airplane changes in flight with respect to the ground or other fixed object, it will rotate about one or more of these axes. Think of these axes as imaginary axles around which the airplane turns, like a wheel. The three axes intersect at the center of gravity and each one is perpendicular to the other.

The imaginary line that extends lengthwise through the fuselage is the *longitudinal axis*. Motion about the longitudinal axis is *roll* and is produced by movement of the ailerons located at the trailing edges of the wings.

The imaginary line which extends crosswise, wingtip to wingtip, is the *lateral axis*. Motion about the lateral axis is *pitch* and is produced by movement of the elevators at the rear of the horizontal tail assembly.

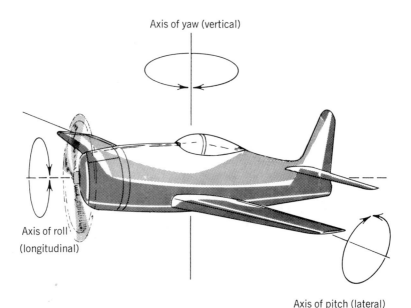

Fig. 2-4.   Axes of rotation around which an airplane turns.

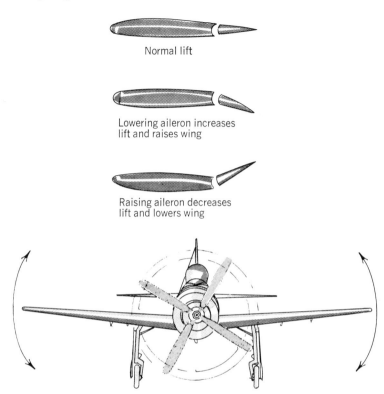

Normal lift

Lowering aileron increases
lift and raises wing

Raising aileron decreases
lift and lowers wing

Fig. 2-5. Action of ailerons which moves the airplane on its longitudinal axis.

The imaginary line which passes vertically through the
center of gravity is the vertical axis. Motion about the vertical
axis is *yaw* and is produced by movement of the rudder located at the rear of the vertical tail assembly.

In order to control the aircraft through the air, there are
ailerons, elevators and rudder surfaces that actually move the
airplane in the direction desired by the pilot. The two *ailerons,* one at the outer trailing edge of each wing, are movable
surfaces that control movement about the longitudinal axis.
The movement is *roll.* Lowering the aileron on one wing
raises the aileron on the other. The wing with the lowered

aileron goes up because of its increased lift and the wing with the raised aileron goes down because of its decreased lift. Thus, the effect of moving either aileron is aided by the simultaneous and opposite movement of the aileron on the other wing.

Rods or cables connect the ailerons to each other and to the control wheel or stick in the cockpit. When pressure is applied to the right on the control wheel, the left aileron goes down and the right aileron goes up, rolling the airplane to the right. This happens because the down movement of

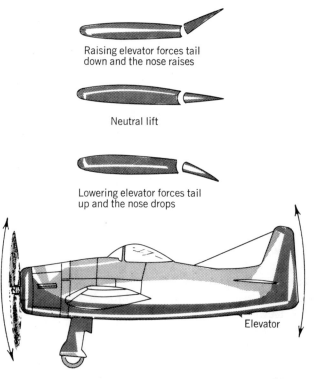

Raising elevator forces tail down and the nose raises

Neutral lift

Lowering elevator forces tail up and the nose drops

Elevator

Fig. 2-6. Action of the elevators which moves the airplane on its lateral axis.

the left aileron increases the wing camber or curvature. The right aileron moves upward and decreases the camber. Thus, decreased lift on the right wing and increased lift on the left wing cause a roll and bank to the right.

The *elevators* control the movement of the airplane about its *lateral* axis. This motion is *pitch*. The elevators form the rear part of the horizontal tail assembly and are free to swing up and down. They are hinged to a fixed surface—the horizontal stabilizer. Together, the horizontal stabilizer and the elevators form a single airfoil. A change in position of the elevators modifies the camber of the airfoil, which increases or decreases lift.

Like the ailerons, the elevators are connected to the control wheel or stick by control cables. When forward pressure is applied on the wheel, the elevators move downward. This increases the lift produced by the horizontal tail surfaces. The increased lift forces the tail upward, causing the nose to drop. Conversely, when back pressure is applied on the wheel, the elevators move upward, decreasing the lift produced by the horizontal tail surfaces, or maybe even producing a downward force. The tail is forced downward and the nose up.

The *rudder* controls movement of the airplane about its vertical axis. This motion is *yaw*. Like the other primary control surfaces, the rudder is a movable surface hinged to a fixed surface, which in this case is the vertical stabilizer, or fin. Its action is very much like that of the elevators, except that it swings in a different plane—from side to side instead of up and down—and is connected by control cables to the rudder pedals.

These are the vital controls in aircraft—no matter how small or how large, how slow or how fast—that are used to fly in the direction desired by the pilot. Modern aircraft also carry guidance systems of many types—called navigational aides.

The first navigational devices consisted primarily of surface features such as terrain and man-made objects. With airborne equipment consisting of only a compass, the early airmail pilots optimistically set off across country, following roads, railroad tracks, streams and small towns. Of course, these flights were mainly carried out in the daytime during good weather. At night, pilots followed fires on the ground set by farmers along the plane's route. The many problems with this system can be visualized—wet wood and the dependability of the men who manned these fires on a somewhat variable schedule.

As the early airmail pioneering years passed, something more dependable than brush fires was required, and electric beacon lights and course lights were installed along the most frequently used air routes. This was a definite improvement,

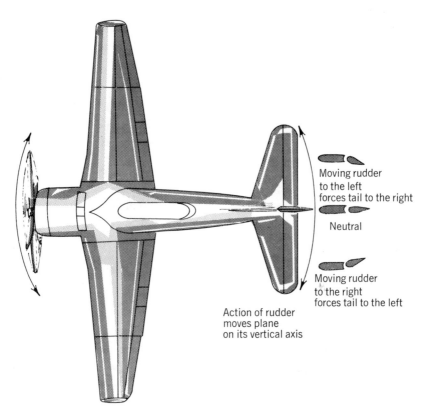

Moving rudder
to the left
forces tail to the right

Neutral

Moving rudder
to the right
forces tail to the left

Action of rudder
moves plane
on its vertical axis

Fig. 2-7.   Effect of rudder in controlling motion of the airplane along its vertical axis.

but these lights were of no help to the pilot caught in poor weather at night. Something was needed which did not depend on visibility, something which would penetrate fog and overcast.

This requirement gave birth to the first electronic highway. This *low frequency range* provided four electronically derived courses which enabled the pilot to determine his directions, thus permitting him to navigate across country by listening to the radio signals or, as pilots refer to it, "flying on the beam."

This was the first airways system. It has since evolved into more refined electronic methods of guidance which help pilots to reach their destinations with complete accuracy.

3

Navigation of Modern Ships

In the harbor, a great ship displacing thousands of tons of water slowly steams toward the open sea. A "pilot," representing the harbor's local port authority, is standing behind the bos'n at the wheel, calmly directing him to steer the ship past other incoming and outgoing vessels, barges and small craft. For the time it takes the "pilot" to direct the ship out of the harbor, he is virtually the captain of the vessel in all but name. For when a ship leaves a harbor as complex as New York or San Francisco, the first part of an intricate and complex control and guidance system goes into effect.

The first element of this guidance and control system is man himself. No matter whether he is aboard a ship, an airplane or a true spacecraft orbiting or leaving the earth, man is the intelligence guiding and controlling the space vehicle —the directing force. Aboard a ship moving out to sea, he is a navigator whose duty is to find and record the position of his ship whenever necessary to establish its position in relation to the direction it is going—and its ultimate destination.

When a ship leaves the dock, a pilot is engaged to guide it out to sea. The pilot, who in a sense is a navigator, is important for two reasons. First, the methods used by the pilot in locating position by means of easily recognized landmarks such as lighthouses, beacons, and tall buildings is essentially the same as that used by the navigator on the high seas. In other words, the basic principles of piloting apply to all navigation. Secondly, the navigator *must* be right. An error made in locating position on the high seas can be detected by later observations; but an error made when piloting, because of the short distances involved, may result in disaster.

The man at the wheel or helm of the ship translates the

course the ship will sail. He receives his instructions, and his period on the bridge—or "watch" as it's referred to by his sailors—is spent keeping the vessel on her proper course. As we noted earlier, the oceans also can be referred to as space, and the ship is a "spacecraft" designed to travel on the surface of the sea. The modern ship—the spacecraft of the sea—had its early beginnings thousands of years ago, when man first took to the water aboard a log, and later a small boat carved from a log. Slowly but surely, as man's intelligence grew, he learned how to propel his boats to their destination by pole, oar, sail and steam.

Ships, or any floating craft, are designed to operate in two fluids of different density—air and water. The density of water is the deciding factor in guiding and controlling a moving vessel which has the buoyancy to float on water, just as a balloon or lighter-than-air vehicle has the buoyancy to float in air. Buoyancy, the force which supports a floating vessel, exists because the density of water is greater than the density of air; this is similar to a balloon filled with helium which rises because air is denser than helium.

Since the sea is a denser fluid than air, the same principles affecting an aircraft in flight (as we have seen in Chapter 2) also affect a ship at sea. Aerial disturbances such as storms have their counterpart at sea, and ships, like aircraft, often travel around a storm rather than through it.

Steering or guiding a ship to its destination is easier said than done. The man at the helm is like the pilot of an airplane; at all times he must know where he is, in order to maintain the course to his destination. The compass tells him if he is heading in the right direction, but he must periodically check his position. At sea, or on flights across the ocean, the basic method is to use the sun—or the stars—to determine location with instruments like a sextant and an accurate clock. This form of navigation is less than 300 years old; but there are many additional electronic aids which help the navigator keep tabs on his location at all times.

With the improvement of radio communications, marine navigation aids received a big boost with the development of the radio direction finder for determining the position of a ship at sea. No longer was weather a problem for the mariner. Radio equipment now permitted sailors—even the weekend sailor in his small cabin cruiser—to home-in on a shore radio station, either with a directional receiver or by triangulating from several shore stations in direct contact with the vessel at sea.

Two wartime developments have also added more sophistication to electronic navigation. *Radar* is of immeasurable value to the navigator for it allows him to "see" his surroundings on a screen when darkness, weather, or both, make any sightings impossible. Radar is of great help in piloting ships off shore or through waters in which other ships are also sailing or at anchor.

Loran, for long-range navigation, unlike radar picks up a steady low frequency signal which permits transmissions over long distances. Ships with Loran equipment can home in on this signal to reach their destinations in all types of weather.

Another new electronic aid is the Transit satellite, an orbiting spacecraft that emits a continuous signal as it passes, permitting navigators to get a "fix" on it and determine their location just as they would get a fix on a star or the sun.

By knowing where his ship is at all times, the navigator at sea can issue correct headings which the helmsman will follow, steering the ship to its destination. Until the advent of the Transit navigation satellites, error on behalf of navigators could be measured in miles and time lost—time which added up to money. Transit has improved navigation and therefore has saved time that was required to correct navigational errors. Moreover, it allows greater margins of safety in passing obstructions. In addition to the savings by faster passages, merchant ship operations have benefited from better maintenance of schedules, and the avoidance of overtime and idle paid time of stevedores used to unload ships.

Sea captains, even in modern times, had been aware that better navigation is particularly required when a vessel approaches landfall after several days at sea. The time required to change course and travel additional distance from landfall to the port of call has added up to dollars and lost profits. Perhaps the mariners most severely hit by the problems of navigation are commercial fishing vessels. Now they can improve their economic situation by returning expeditiously to favorable fishing areas instead of cruising around trying to discover where the schools of fish were last located.

For navigation at sea or in flight, the new navigation satellites serve the same purpose that a natural celestial body does in ordinary celestial navigation, except that radio or other electronic signals are used instead of optical sightings. Coupled with man himself, navigational aids at sea make possible the journeys by ship to the far corners of the earth.

4

Principles of Rocket Power and Flight

As man began to travel farther and faster, he devised methods of controlling and guiding the craft in which he travelled. His first experiments in controlling direction and speed were with projectiles of a defensive and offensive nature. Feathers on arrows and spears controlled the direction of these weapons. Later, man developed equipment to hurl heavy objects a greater distance against an enemy. He was forced to build the first catapults when defense fortifications grew larger and stronger. Catapults could hurl 100-pound boulders a distance of 600 yards.

They were also used to hurl pots of fire behind enemy walls as well as the carcasses of dead animals in early attempts at germ warfare. The development of equipment to hurl heavy objects signalled the arrival of artillery and, in a primitive sense, the space age was germinated once power was placed behind weapons to give them hurtling ability.

The development of gunpowder was so effective that artillery came to be referred to as "the last argument of kings." And with that development, it was just a matter of time before the rocket and missile made its appearance. Actually, the origin of gunpowder and rockets and missiles is lost in time. However, legend and fact have given us some place at which to start.

The Chinese were said to have used gunpowder as early as 300 A.D., and rockets against the Tartars in 1232. But gunpowder didn't actually revolutionize warfare until 1248 when Friar Roger Bacon described how a mixture of carbon, sulphur and potassium nitrate would explode when ignited. Legend has it that winged rocketry began in Sixteenth Century China. Wan Hu, an official of that era, conceived an approach to manned rocket flight that called for equipping a sedan chair with 47 solid-propellant rockets. The entire unit was suspended between two kites which might have been intended to lift it above the atmosphere, or perhaps were merely meant to align the craft for launching. Wan Hu's ground crew consisted of 47 coolies, rehearsed to light 47 matches simultaneously. On the momentous day of launching they touched their matches, on signal, to the 47 fuses. Moments later, a tremendous explosion reverberated along the great wall of China. Unidentifiable debris fluttered down on the countryside. It is not very likely that Wan Hu reached escape velocity and is orbiting somewhere within this solar system or another galaxy—but more probably he became a part of the fluttering debris.

The use of rocket weapons during the Middle Ages declined with the development of cannon, although the rocket continued to be used as a signalling device and for fireworks display purposes. Attempts to develop the rockets as weapons began again in the Eighteenth Century; our history books tell us that during the War of 1812 the British used rockets against Fort McHenry in Baltimore harbor. The rockets, whose "red glare" is so vividly recorded in "The Star Spangled Banner," were not signal flares, but carried warheads loaded with substantial amounts of explosive—"the bombs bursting in air" described in our national anthem.

The modern rocket had its origin in the research work carried out by Robert H. Goddard, acknowledged to be the father of American rocketry. During World War I he actually designed rocket weapons, which were the basis of similar weapons used during World War II. Unfortunately, his vision for the use of rockets as weapons brought nothing but disdain from the generals of 1914–18 who were steeped in the military traditions of the Civil War. Nevertheless, Goddard continued his research in rocketry, and a number of his patents held essential features that were later incorporated by the Germans into V-1 and V-2 rocket weapons.

The dreaded V-1 and V-2 flying bombs during World War II were the forerunners of the first ballistic missiles, along with the Russian Katusha rocket launching battery and the famous Bazooka, favored by GIs to knock out tanks. These weapons all worked on the same principle. À specific amount of fuel would ignite and burn for a short time, giving the missile itself enough push to send it on its way to the target at a high rate of speed.

Its velocity would determine its direction. When velocity petered out it would fall on its target. In the case of the V-2 rocket, or flying bomb, a simple guidance system based on the amount of fuel used for launching, altitude and direction would bring it to the target area without pinpoint accuracy. It would fall in a specific area, and its huge explosive warhead would do the rest.

Actually, the very fundamentals of rocket flight give some direction to a basic missile. A rocket's speed or velocity will hold it on course for a specific amount of time. When this velocity decreases, the rocket will drop to earth. We must understand the rocket and what makes it go, in order to grasp the later sophisticated guidance and control systems being installed in spacecraft.

Behind the principle of rocket flight is Newton's third law of motion: That any action on an object is accompanied by an equal and opposite reaction. The rocket propellant provides the velocity force or reaction by burning in a combustive chamber, thereby generating a gas at high temperature and pressure. It is the escape of this gas through the exit nozzle that pushes the rocket forward. The rearward momentum of the escaping gas provides the forward momentum, and velocity, of the rocket.

In modern times, the first man to harness rocket power to a winged craft was the German automobile manufacturer, Fritz von Opel. His early experiments, conducted with racing cars, convinced him that rocket power could be utilized on aircraft. In the spring of 1928, he rigged a glider with several solid-propellant rocket motors, which were to be fired after the glider was launched with a tow rope. His first flight, a complete success though it covered a distance of only about a mile, spurred him on to more challenging flights. On September 30, 1929, he made the first rocket-powered takeoff. His glider was guided on the takeoff run by a wooden track. As it became airborne and attained a speed of approximately 100 miles an hour, von Opel fired the remaining six rockets mounted under the wings. Insulating materials, however, had either been ignored or miscalculated, for the glider's wings caught fire. In his anxiety to get the craft back on the ground, von Opel crashed. He crawled away, none the worse for wear, from one of the shortest manned rocket flights on record but a milestone in technique.

While winged rocketry was undergoing its birth, stove pipe rocketry research continued in the United States, Germany, Russia and England; paid for out of parsimonious research funds. Pipes filled with many chemical mixtures of solid and liquid propellants were used to launch these early exploratory rockets anywhere from one to 20 miles high. Each altitude record meant that another rocket scientist in another country

Fig. 4-1. Limb of the earth as seen by John Glenn through the window of Friendship 7 spacecraft. (NASA)

had to try to top the previous record. It goes without saying that some tragic accidents occurred when highly explosive rocket fuels blew up on the pad, injuring and killing some of the early pioneers.

It was left for winged rocket flight research to improve rocket, and later missile technology. The Germans led in rocket research in the mid-1930s, with Dr. Wernher von Braun, now a top American space scientist, pioneering some of the later research in winged rocket flight. In 1941, U.S. Army Air Force Captain Homer Boushey, working with a scientific group from the University of California, conducted an experiment which marked the first United States introduction of rocket power to the airplane.

A small low-wing monoplane, the Ercoupe, was made available to Captain Boushey to enable him to conduct flight tests in rocket-assisted takeoff. Three solid-propellant rocket units were attached to the underside of each wing. Each unit was designed so that both the exhaust nozzle and the combustion chamber were free to fly clear of the airplane in case of an explosion. On August 6, 1941, Captain Boushey took off in the early morning hours from March Field, California. On this first flight, the rocket units were utilized merely as an assist in takeoff; in later flights, they were used for propulsion power.

Rocket power for manned aircraft was further developed during World War II by the Germans, who mass-produced the ME-163—the first rocket-propelled aircraft actually to see combat. American fighter pilots flying in P-47 Thunderbolts and P-51 Mustangs, then considered the fastest fighter planes in combat, told of the fantastic speeds of the ME-163 Komet which actually fired on U.S. aircraft.

After World War II, the United States and the Soviet Union turned their research from manned winged rockets to unmanned missiles. It was on this note of research that the space age was born.

5

Navigation

We are now travelling faster and farther than ever before. As a result of this spurt in speed and distance, navigators have had to know where they were at all times, in relation to their destination. Finding the answer to this question has always been one of the most complex problems man is called upon to solve. This question is so difficult, in fact, that to answer it we have had to develop an entire science—the science of navigation.

In previous chapters we have just touched on this subject, but navigation is an integral part of the control and guidance of spacecraft. In simple terms, navigation is the process of steering to a destination. It is usually accomplished by determining the craft's present position and then plotting the course it must follow to reach its destination.

In the case of a ship, for example, and the word "navigate" originally meant "to steer a ship," the navigator can draw a line on the earth representing the shortest distance between two points, say New York and London, and try to follow it. We say *try* to stay on it because the vessel will always deviate from its original course due to the action of wind, ocean currents or errors in piloting. The navigator, therefore, must determine his new position from time to time and redirect his vessel.

The advent of power gave the pilot, or helmsman, greater control and reduced the amount of deviation from the desired route, but the navigator's problem remained essentially the same. The same problem confronts the pilot of an airplane, with the complication that he operates in an additional or third dimension—altitude. He may solve his problem in the same way as the ancient ship navigator—or he may use a more modern method known as homing. There are many types of homing devices today, but the essential principle is familiar to almost everyone in the form of the radio homing system which, as we have discussed earlier, has had a profound effect on modern aviation. Essentially, a continuous electronic signal is followed by the airplane to its destination.

Point-to-point plotting and homing are the two basic navigational systems that man uses on earth, and much of our history can be told in terms of new achievements in the art of navigation. The magnetic compass, for example, was one of the most revolutionary technical discoveries in history. Without it, the great age of exploration which culminated in the modern world could never have come to pass.

The compass needle, which aligns itself with the earth's lines of magnetic force flowing roughly north to south, gives the navigator a known direction from which to calculate. And calculate he must. Over the centuries, navigators have developed mathematical formulas to a fine degree as an aid to determining their location in reference to their destination.

The emphasis, however, has been on man and the methods he has devised to travel from one place to another. Man himself has been the guidance and control system for whatever his mode of transportation. It wasn't until the past hundred years that man began to understand himself as a control system; and it appears that he is one of the best analogies.

From the time he is a child learning how to walk, man develops his five senses, which he constantly uses to guide and control his movements and actions. These sensing channels are sight, hearing, smell, taste and touch, without which he could not survive—even in a friendly environment like his own backyard. The brain supervises motion and interprets what the senses "feel." A pilot flying by the "seat of his pants" may *think* he is flying straight and level, but the senses work only so far. That is why man is building additional senses to complement what he already has. Various types of instruments, like the turn and bank indicator in an airplane, or a stall warning indicator, sense the correct attitude of the aircraft before the pilot does. These aids sound an alarm and the pilot can then correct what his own senses cannot determine.

The advancement of aviation and the birth of the space age have now forced us to build electronic brains operated by skilled people. These artificial brains are aids to man; he makes the final decisions, based on the information provided him by this artificial extension of his own basic senses.

Now we shall see how man was given a sixth sense with the development of the *gyroscope*. Heretofore, man totally lacked the ability to sense most of his movements in *space*. On the other hand, he had not developed long-distance ship, aircraft and space travel. The development of this sixth sense, therefore, came in its own good time—when man was ready to use it.

One of the most important basic features of all matter is a state of equilibrium, or balance, whereby the molecular

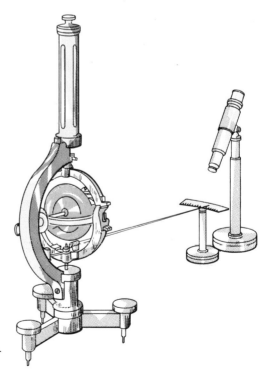

Fig. 5-1.   Foucault's instrument.

structure of atoms retains a balanced orbit of particles spinning around each other. In fact, ever since matter started rotating about a point in space, a *gyroscopic* action was created which is as old as the universe. Sir Isaac Newton didn't refer to this phenomenon as gyroscopic action, but he incorporated it into his basic laws of motion—specifically, in the principle that a body once put in motion will continue to move in the same direction, unless influenced by external forces.

It was left to Leon Foucault, the famous French scientist, to coin the word gyroscope when he produced the first visible demonstration of the earth's rotation, and by the simplest of all mechanical devices—a swinging pendulum. Foucault, however, wished to corroborate his experiment by a device that would be truly independent of the earth—a freely-mounted rotating wheel. Such an instrument had been known for a quarter of a century but had been used only for demonstrating its own characteristics. He constructed a delicately mounted wheel which could be spun at a high rate of speed in a supporting ring, or gimbal, suspended by a twistless thread of silk. With this instrument, he was able to show in a convincing way that the earth revolved while the axle of the wheel maintained its fixed position in regard to space.

Foucault selected the term "gyroscope," which means "to view the revolution of the earth," because this new instrument actually made the rotation of the earth visible. Many years elapsed before anyone else found any further use for a gyroscope other than as a scientific instrument. In a practical application, the gyro wheel had to be capable of sustained spinning for hours, days or even weeks; but friction at the points made this impossible. Further development had to await the invention of the electric motor and also the development of ball bearings, which could support a heavy gyroscope running at high speed without quickly wearing out. But Foucault, having demonstrated the earth's rotation by means of a gyroscope, predicted that the gyro would one day be used as a compass.

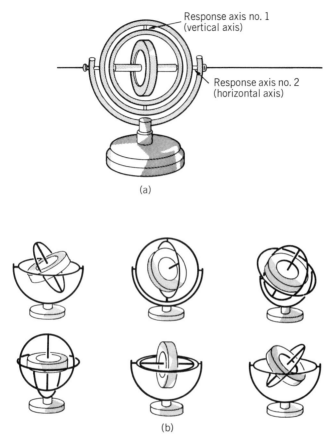

Fig. 5-2. Gyroscopic motion. (a) The gyroscope has two degrees of freedom; the assembly can turn about a vertical axis (response axis number 1) and also about a horizontal axis (response axis number 2). (b) The axle of a gyroscope can be pointed in any direction without altering the geometrical center of the assembly.

The gyroscopes that followed consisted of a spinning mass or wheel, universally mounted, so that only one point—its center of gravity—is in a fixed position, with the wheel being free to turn in any direction around this point.

One example of gyroscopic action is the earth itself. The theory that the earth at one time was a part of the sun and was set spinning when it was thrown off the parent celestial body is now accepted by many scientists. It is a fact, however, that the earth does spin and was spinning long before any living thing could be found on its surface. The *gyroscope*, then, is the oldest mechanism known, because the earth itself is a gyroscope.

The study of celestial mechanics tells us that the earth spins around its axis at a very high speed for such an enormous body; any point at its equator travels at a speed of more than 1,000 miles per hour. This compares with the 30 to 250 miles per hour peripheral speed, which is the general range for man-made gyros. The earth may be said to be celestially mounted freely in space, and as far as our lifetime is concerned, it will keep its axis constantly in one direction—namely, within one degree of the North Star. Moreover, it keeps spinning away without friction. This fixed spin axis is one of the basic properties of the gyroscope, and this same movement in man-made gyros is the basis of many modern navigational and guidance instruments.

A second property of the gyroscope is a peculiar motion called precession. It occurs when a force tries to change the direction of its spinning axis. In the case of the earth, there is a very slight force trying to change the spinning axis. It is caused by the off-center pull of the sun's gravity on the tilted bulge of the earth's equator. This causes the earth's axis to sweep out a cone in space—called the precession of the equinox—which it goes around once in about 26,000 years.

A modern idea of the gyroscope implies gimbal rings, torque motors, gas bearings, jewel pivots, flotation, high speeds and integration, but the early unrecognizable gyroscope actually began as a toy. The first artificial gyros were probably made by the Chinese and were what we now call spinning tops. The spinning top keeps its axis pointing in a constant direction unless it is leaning out of the vertical, in which case it describes a cone just as the earth does, but with a much quicker motion. This precession is caused by a coupling of two forces which are the force of gravity pulling the top downwards and the pressure of the supporting surface upwards on the point. If the top leans, the two forces are not in line. Nobody knows when the first spinning top was made, but it was certainly the earliest example of a scientific toy. Another example is the coin rolling on its edge across the floor. Gyroscopic action is also involved here. If the coin were simply standing on edge, instead of rolling, and began tipping toward the side, the action (pull) of gravity would cause it to fall flat on the floor. When it is rolling and tips to one side, gyroscopic action causes it to turn in the direction toward which it tips, until the effect of the centrifugal force introduced balances that of gravity. The coin will therefore roll in a smaller and tighter circle as its speed decreases.

In the early part of this century, a variety of gyroscopic tops made their appearance. They were spun with a piece of string and behaved in a most "mysterious" manner because at the time few people had ever heard of "fixity in space" or "precession." When one end of the frame was placed on a small support or pivot, the spinning toy appeared to defy the law of gravity, since it would not fall down until the speed of its spin decreased.

Another example of gyroscopic action so important to guidance and control of ballistic missiles, and manned and unmanned rocket-booster powered wingless spacecraft, is the

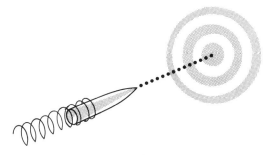

Fig. 5-3. The spin of the bullet stabilizes its flight to the target.

bullet. Just who it was that first thought of grooving the bore of a firearm to make the bullet spin, and thus travel more accurately and farther, is lost in the shades of history. Perhaps it was some person who had observed the spinning of a top. At any rate, the rifle was almost certainly the first useful application of a gyroscopic principle, and it came at least 300 years before the first experimental gyroscope was put together.

A bullet, if not spinning, tends to tumble end over end in its flight to the target. The rifling of the barrel, however, imparts a rapid spinning motion which forces the bullet to act as a miniature gyroscope whose action causes the projectile to correct automatically for any tendency of its axis to deviate from the direct line to the target. For this reason, the bullet flies straight and true.

The gyroscope, as we have seen, is the instrument basic to guiding and controlling all manner of moving craft. Its application is of the utmost importance to holding course during any journey—whether it be on land, at sea, undersea, in the air or through limitless space.

6

Gyroscope Principles

"A Compass of a spinning kind
Is also toward the north inclined;
An iron ship it doesn't mind.
The axis of its spinning wheel
Is quite oblivious to steel
In turret, funnel, deck or keel."
　　　　—from "Reflections" by an officer
　　　　of the Royal Navy

Early in this century it was theorized that the gyroscope could produce the same kind of information as the magnetic compass—but more accurately. Seafarers at the turn of the century were faced with a serious problem as the wooden sailing ships manned by iron men were replaced by ships of steel powered by steam. When he learned his trade, the seafaring navigator knew that the compass had great value. After all, hadn't the pirate Captain Kidd listed "One large Lode Stone" in the inventory of his precious treasure that was dug up and turned over to the British Crown in 1699. Such was the importance of direction to the navigator. For though the magnetic compass had been used for several hundred years, there was still no way—not even in Captain Kidd's time—of magnetizing the needle of a mariner's compass, unless one had a lodestone with which to stroke it. Generations of navigators travelled with their lodestones until the time came when steel finally displaced wood in the construction of ships. Then the navigator's problem became unbearably acute.

The problem in this case was simple. The U.S. Navy required a new and reliable compass for its battleships. The magnetic compass, with which all ships at the time were equipped, was vastly less trustworthy in a steel hull than it had been in wooden ships. The needle had a tendency to follow every swing of the gun turret; even the changes of temperature in the smokestack could turn the compass haywire.

The problem was solved by Dr. Elmer Sperry, who harnessed the compass and the gyroscope to a combination he called the Gyro-Compass. What Sperry did was utilize the combined effects of the earth's rotation and the force of gravity in order to keep the gyro axle in line with the earth's meridian, that imaginary great circle that passes through the poles. He thus provided navigators with a True North indicator, which required no compensation in calculations like those necessary in a magnetic compass pointing only to the earth's magnetic poles.

Since the introduction of the Sperry-Gyro-Compass in 1911, man has developed an almost uncountable number of navigational devices—all of them sophisticated variations of the fundamental navigational techniques we have been discussing. The birth of instrument flying is relatively new. "Blind" flight used to be a common term in aviation because a pilot was practically blind as soon as clouds, fog or darkness kept him from seeing the horizon. The change from "blind" to "instrument flying" was due entirely to improved new flight instruments.

In the fall of 1929, a young man named Jimmy Doolittle carried on some experiments in blind flying. In discussions with several engineers he pointed out that progress depended upon the development of some instrument that would show the pilot the relationship of his plane to the horizon at all times—and instantly. This was another creation of man's sixth sense.

A few weeks later, Lieutenant Doolittle, a pilot in the old Army Air Corps, took off from Mitchell Field, Long Island, seated in a plane with a hooded cockpit. He circled the field and landed without seeing outside the cockpit. This historic flight was accomplished entirely on instruments. Specifically, the development of the Artificial Horizon and the Directional Gyro made this epic feat possible.

The Gyro-Horizon, as the artificial horizon is known, provided an accurate substitute for the real horizon and made it unnecessary to have outside visibility. The pilot could "fly" a miniature airplane on the face of the instrument on his panel. This miniature airplane was set in relation to an artificial horizon bar that was kept horizontal by a tiny, 12-ounce gyroscope spinning at high speed. With this instrument, which was simple and natural to use, the pilot could climb or dive, or bank in either direction and still be aware of his attitude to the real horizon at all times.

The Directional Gyro had an azimuth scale graduated in degrees and stabilized by an airdriven gyroscope whose spin axis was horizontal. The Directional Gyro could be set to agree with the magnetic compass heading, and once set, it could be relied upon to provide accurate, dead-beat directional indications for periods up to 15 or 20 minutes. Keeping a straight course by Directional Gyro permitted the magnetic compass to settle, at which time the pilot could check his compass course and reset the Directional Gyro if necessary.

By 1932 these two instruments had won international acclaim by their contributions toward the success of the epoch-making flights of that era. Poor flying conditions caused by thick weather was a thing of the past. Wiley Post, following his first round-the-world flight in the "Winnie Mae" with Harold Gatty, attributed this successful feat to the two new flight instruments. "Both instruments," he later reported, "functioned perfectly throughout. . . . We flew four straight hours between Siberia and Nome without being able to see outside the ship, and our success in getting through was due to our implicit faith in these instruments."

The natural outgrowth of these two instruments was the Gyro or Automatic Pilot which Wiley Post used in his second record-breaking round-the-world flight. This new Automatic Pilot had a built-in Directional Gyro and Gyro-Horizon, and from the flight references supplied by these instruments, an air pick-off system actuated hydraulic pistons which operated the aircraft's rudder, ailerons and elevators. Flying solo through every kind of imaginable weather and over vast wastes of land and sea, Post broke every previous record—a great improvement on his earlier flight with Gatty, in which the "Winnie Mae" was flown entirely manually.

With the Automatic Pilot on the job, Post was free to study his maps, operate the radio and watch for landmarks through the occasional holes in the clouds—and even sleep! Holding a wrench tied to a finger, he would doze while the Automatic Pilot continued to fly the plane. When he fell sound asleep his hand relaxed, the wrench fell, jerked his finger and woke him up.

"I had four times as much bad weather as on my previous world flight," Post wrote, "and I believe it would have been impossible for anyone to have come through such weather without the Automatic Pilot."

Such was the auspicious beginning of a 9 × 14-inch box, which was immune to fatigue, held a true course, and steadily controlled and guided an airplane on a series of long hops.

7

Inertial Guidance Systems

The new navigational, guidance and control instrumentation we have just covered was predicated on the single question mariners, pilots, and travelers have always asked themselves while en route to their destination. Where am I? Now, man is embarking on a new journey in another environment called space. Until today, or perhaps we should say the day before yesterday, man's navigational ingenuity has been concerned with moving himself from place to place on his own planet. But now man is venturing into space. How will he navigate there? How will he control and guide his spacecraft?

How will he answer the astronaut's two basic and challenging questions: Where am I? What must I do to reach my destination?

When travelling in space we must take into consideration that our earth is a vehicle moving at tremendous speed in an elliptical orbit about our sun. Earth is actually one of a fleet of vehicles revolving about a star—the sun—which is itself in motion through the galaxy of which we are a minute part. Our nearest neighbor—the moon—is rotating about us 230,000 miles away. To reach the moon we must aim, not at where it is when we set out for our lunar destination, but at where it will be many hours later when we get there. In space, we will not rocket to a fixed destination—we will *rendezvous* with it.

In the word *rendezvous* is summed up the one essential difference between the problems of the earthbound navigators of yesterday and the astronauts of today and tomorrow. Where the earthbound navigator can expect his point of departure and his destination to remain in fixed relation to each other, this will never be true for the astronaut. There is still another question connected with this word *rendezvous,* a question of immediate and pressing importance. That question is: Rendezvous with what?

The space around us is already alive with man-made objects travelling endlessly on journeys of their own while the planet revolves beneath them. So far, their purpose has been research, and they have all proved harmless. But the military aspects of space flight are shaping some of our future progress in space. The problems of destroying or shooting down a hostile object from space might seem to be more a problem of ballistics, or marksmanship, than navigation. It is a problem of guidance and control—and then navigation, so that inspection of a hostile satellite can be carried out. Navigation, in short, begins where ballistics and marksmanship end.

Man himself has already entered space, but in his early efforts he has been merely a passenger on an orbiting missile, his flight a result of good marksmanship rather than navigation. However, space flight will be practical with the Gemini and Apollo spacecraft that will permit astronauts to choose their point of landing after launching from fixed takeoff areas. These future launchings must be made with an equal certainty of astronauts returning from space when they desire, and where they choose to land on earth.

To make navigation, guidance, control and rendezvous in space possible, we have developed what's called an inertial guidance system. Specifically, this is a technique or process for directing ships, submarines, aircraft, missiles and spaceships to selected destinations or targets. Inertial guidance systems provide information about the actual path of the vehicle in relation to a predetermined path. Any differences are transmitted to the vehicle's control system. An inertial guidance system performs these functions without seeking information from outside the spacecraft.

What this system does is store and retain the preset flight instructions very accurately, then automatically compensate for any changes in direction by computing time, distance and, in the case of space flight, the various forces reacting on the spacecraft.

Strangely enough, the inertial guidance system used on space vehicles was first developed for aircraft, ships and submarines—for use in the air and beneath the sea. As an autopilot in high speed aircraft, inertial guidance systems measured factors applicable to winged flight. Beneath the sea, it measured various factors reacting upon submarines. In nuclear-powered submarines, the system is called SINS, for Ship's Inertial Navigation System. In 1957 SINS made it possible for the submarine Nautilus to travel, completely submerged, from the east coast to the sea beneath the north polar ice cap and return—without once surfacing for a navigator to take a fix on the sun or stars.

As air supports planes, the sea also supports "flying" vehicles like the submarine. Its elongated shape resembles a spaceship, and some of the forces reacting on the submarine are similar to the forces reacting on spacecraft.

There is one similarity that spacecraft and submarines both have. During flight a spacecraft has to be positioned, just as a submarine must be positioned in relation to its immediate environment. The SINS developed for use underwater is actually a stabilizer which makes it possible for the undersea boat to keep a steady keel, despite the various shifts caused by rough seas. An autopilot aboard an aircraft utilizing an inertial guidance system would work in a similar manner, stabilizing the airplane in rough weather.

The value of the inertial guidance system in the submarine along with stabilizing this type of underwater "spacecraft" has made it possible for nuclear-powered under-sea boats to travel thousands of miles without surfacing and to arrive at various destinations "on the button."

As a result, several spacecraft inertial guidance systems are now based on the submarine's SINS. The Polaris submarine, a marvel of military engineering, can roam beneath the oceans for months at a time. Moreover, this nuclear-powered "sub" combines different types of spaceflight—its own "flight" through the sea fluid and the flight of its missiles through water, air and space. Its Polaris missiles can be fired from underwater to targets more than 2,500 miles away. As a mobile platform for this awesome missile, the Polaris submarine is of great strategic military value—but only if it works accurately.

This is where the submarine's own inertial guidance system comes into play, as well as the inertial guidance system aboard its missiles. The effectiveness of the entire Polaris weapons system hinges on the ability of a submarine skipper to know where he is at all times, not merely within miles, but within a few hundred yards. And the less he has to bring his sub to the surface, the more freedom and safety he has.

Unless the precise position of the submarine is known, its missiles may be sent off on a course that may seem like a small deviation at the start, but that goes dozens of miles astray at the limits of their range. The error increases as the range expands.

Before a Polaris missile is fired, its guidance system must be told two things: the distance to target, and the exact course to take. If the distance is miscalculated by a mile, the missile will miss the target by just a mile, assuming other factors to be equal. This is not considered a significant error when the thermonuclear warhead carries the equivalent of tens of thousands of tons of TNT. But if the aim is off, the Polaris will miss badly.

The ideal guidance and control system for a Polaris sub would be 100 per cent accurate and would never require the sub to expose its position by coming to the surface. Such a system continues to elude scientists and engineers, so the Navy uses a series of devices to achieve the precision it needs.

The SINS aboard the Polaris submarine is composed of an array of precision gyros and accessory electronic equipment designed to keep track of the submarine's every movement—its true heading, its speed, its geographical position. Each submarine carries three SINS systems, two of them merely to keep a double check on the first.

If SINS were perfect—not just $99\frac{44}{100}$ per cent perfect—a Polaris sub would never have to come near the ocean surface for navigation purposes. But, like any other machinery, it is subject to an irreducible minimum of error, so it is necessary periodically to check SINS against some point of reference. Nowadays, the Polaris skipper brings the sub up to periscope depth, allowing the navigator to use a special periscope for a fix on three stars. Of course, a celestial fix depends on weather; in northern latitudes, during winter, cloudy conditions may last for days, preventing any glimpse of the stars.

Therefore, the Navy has also equipped all its Polaris submarines with Loran equipment. Loran (long-range navigation) was developed during World War II but has been improved greatly in recent years.

Early versions of Loran had a range of about 600 miles, providing accuracy within about five miles. The Loran system now in use has a 1,200-mile range; at extreme range, it is accurate within a quarter-mile, and at 500 miles or so, within a few hundred yards. Loran stations on shore send out continuous signals. A ship must receive signals from these stations to get an accurate fix by triangulation.

Navigational aids developed by the Navy, like the Transit satellite system, ultimately will find important use in space flight. By picking up the continuous radio signal from one or more transit satellites, a ship or submarine navigator should be able to pinpoint his position in a minute or two within a range of about 100 yards.

The satellite orbits will be known precisely; the vessel's position in relation to the orbit can be determined by studying the change in frequency of the Transit's signal as it approaches and then recedes from the ship.

Another new development is the electrostatic gyro (known as the ESG monitor) which should be so accurate that it is equivalent to a celestial fix—"star in a bottle," Navy men call it. A submarine will never have to surface and poke its periscope or antenna up to get a fix confirming SINS readings.

The gyro consists of a twin rotor (the only moving parts) suspended in a vacuum by a high-voltage electrostatic field. In the "hard" (nearly perfect) vacuum and with no physical suspension, the gyro will be virtually free from friction. Once it is brought up to operating speed, it will be able to record precisely a submarine's every motion for month after month.

The ESG monitor and the Transit navigation system may be backed up by underwater beacons that dot the ocean floors. These beacons could be difficult to establish and operate and the system is a long way from practical use. But it would retain the advantage of not requiring a submarine to expose itself on or near the surface.

The idea is to anchor the underwater lighthouses, emitting some sort of fairly short-range signal, about 200 ft. above the ocean floor. They would be powered by small SNAP (systems for nuclear auxiliary power) units that would generate for two years or more.

These devices would send signals for only five or 10 miles, so that a submarine would have to use other methods of navigation to get within their range, then home in on them to find their precise position. Like conventional lighthouses, their signals would be coded for identification.

8

Use of Inertial Guidance Systems with Computers

The success of guiding and controlling all spacecraft moving in three dimensions to a prescribed destination or on a prescribed course, is made possible by *inertial guidance*—the use of completely self-contained gyroscopes. Actually, inertial guidance is a form of completely automatic navigation. It is used on submarines, aircraft and manned and unmanned spacecraft. Without inertial guidance, all travel at high speeds and for long distances would be impossible.

The basic principles of inertial guidance can be likened to the system employed by sea captains hundreds of years ago, when they used dead reckoning to estimate position on the basis of speed, direction and elapsed time. They only needed to know where they started from. Inertial guidance utilizes these same facts, except that now a high speed computer, instead of the human brain, does the rest of the job of compiling facts, analyzing them and coming up with the answers. Inertial guidance is so new that less than 20 years ago navigators aboard huge ocean liners could only come within five or 10 miles of estimating their exact position—even in clear weather. Today, inertial navigation eliminates this error as well as guesswork. What it does not do is produce precise measurements of everything that happens to a moving body; it compares the result of the desired position and then makes corrections to keep it on course—right to its destination.

An example of inertia is the tendency of motionless objects to remain motionless, and of moving objects to stay in motion unless an outside force comes into play. For example, a passenger hanging on a strap in a bus feels a tug on his arm when the bus begins to move. This is caused by the inertia

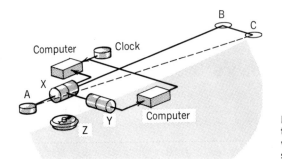

Fig. 8-1. Theoretical inertial-guidance system for a
vehicle moving over a flat
surface.

of his body. It continues as long as the bus keeps increasing
speed. When it reaches a steady speed, the tug disappears.
When the bus slows down, a push instead of a pull is felt. This
is caused by his body's tendency to stay in motion.

The problem then is to measure motion; one of the integral
parts of an inertial guidance system is the accelerometer,
which measures only the *changes* in velocity or motion. It
does not measure velocity or distance. With these facts in
mind, it is apparent that the problem of getting from one
place to another would be quite simple—if it were not for the
fact that we must travel over a spherical surface which is itself
in rotation and is possessed of a mysterious force called gravity.

If we were travelling over a flat surface that did not move
and had no gravitational force, our inertial guidance system
would require only the instruments' shown in Fig. 8-1: two
accelerometers, two computers, a timepiece and compass.
Here A is the starting point, B the destination. X is an accelerometer installed parallel to the desired course AB. Y is
an accelerometer at right angles to X. The Compass Z is
required to keep the meter at right angles to X. The Compass
Z is required to keep the accelerometer pointed in the right
direction. As the vehicle starts and moves on its course from
A to B, accelerometer X supplies its computer with a continuous measure of acceleration. The timepiece supplies the
computer with elapsed time. The computer integrates this
information and produces an indication of the distance
travelled.

If the vehicle continued to move along the course AB, the output of accelerometer Y at right angles to X would be zero; it would have no effect upon the problem. Any movement of the vehicle, which is not parallel to the course AB, movements which might be caused by winds or currents, would affect accelerometer Y, resulting in a signal to its computer, which, integrated with the elapsed time, would correct the course, of the vehicle so that it would arrive at B, and not some other point such as C.

In actual practice, however, we must travel over the curved surface of a globe which has a force of gravity always pulling toward its center. To complicate things a bit further, the earth itself is in rotation and has a magnetic field varying so greatly over its surface that a magnetic compass would be useless as a means to orient our accelerometers.

If the accelerometers are not kept at right angles to the force of gravity at all times, serious errors will be introduced. This is because an accelerometer cannot distinguish between vehicular accelerations which it should measure, and gravity accelerations, which it should ignore. To prevent gravity from affecting the accelerometers, they are placed on a mount or platform stabilized about its horizontal axes by gyroscopes. This is the stable platform so often mentioned with reference to inertial guidance. Its function is to keep the accelerometers horizontal (or perpendicular to the force of gravity), regardless of the angular motioñ of the vehicle or of its position

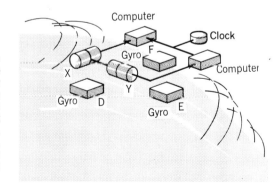

Fig. 8-2. A stabilized platform for an inertial-guidance system consists basically of the two accelerometers X and Y at right angles, a direction gyro D to orient the platform true north, and two gyros, E and F, which keep the platform level about its horizontal axes.

relative to the earth. The stable platform is made stable directionally by adding a third gyroscope which orients it about the vertical axis.

We now have the basic elements of a true inertial navigation system. Actually, a number of other factors have to be compensated for; among them are the earth's bulge at the equator and the "Coriolis effect" (which means that, because the earth itself is rotating, a vehicle has to take a curved path in space to make good a straight course over the earth).

In actual practice, inertial navigation data can be fed into an automatic pilot to control the aircraft or ship, and it can be presented to a human navigator in terms of his actual position in degrees of latitude and longitude, or his distance made good along a great circle or rhumb line course.

The explanation given above is based on one particular system of inertial navigation. Actually, many variations are possible.

Two types of computers, analog and digital, are used in inertial guidance systems. The overall system requirements will determine which is the more satisfactory to use.

Everyday examples of the analog computer are the engineers' slide rule, or the speedometer of an automobile which measures shaft speed and presents its information in the form of a rate indication in terms of miles per hour. Everyday examples of the digital computer are the adding machine, or the odometer of an automobile, which counts the shaft revolutions and presents its information in terms of miles traveled.

Broadly speaking, the computers in an inertial navigation system take the information from the basic instruments (the accelerometers and gyroscopes), digest it, and present it in usable form as aircraft or ship position, distance traveled, or control signals for automatic piloting. Computers may combine a large number of mechanical and electronic devices to carry out the variety of detailed operations required.

Inertial guidance systems coupled with rocket power make space flight possible. But the basic ingredient of successful flights into space is in the knowledge of ballistics—the physical laws governing the motion of projectiles and satellites.

9

Ballistics and Trajectories

The space age definition of a ballistic missile is a vehicle whose flight path, from engine fuel burn-out to impact, is "free flight" like that of an artillery projectile. It is subject to gravitation and drag, and it may or may not perform maneuvers to modify or correct its flight path.

Primitive man had no definition of a ballistic missile other than his use of a rock that he threw to kill an animal or to do battle with an enemy. The ballistic missile is the rock in David's sling that killed Goliath or the arrow shot from a bow. The ballistic missile is the early rocket launched by the ancient Chinese, the huge boulders flung against the enemy from catapults, and later the cannon ball and musket ball. These were the first ballistic missiles.

Each of these missiles follow what is known as the ballistic trajectory, which is shaped by the physical laws of mass in motion. A simple example of a ballistic trajectory is that of a rock after it is thrown from a cliff. The rock traces a nearly parabolic path in accordance with the laws of motion of a body under the force of gravity. In practice, the path is somewhat more complicated because of air resistance, possible wind forces, and the Coriolis effect associated with the spin of Earth about its axis.

The trajectory itself is the path described by a body moving in space. In accord with Newton's Laws of Motion, the trajectory of any body in motion through space depends on (1) its initial velocity and direction; (2) other forces, if any, which are applied to it while in the powered phase of flight, as is the case with rockets; and (3) gravitation forces arising from the proximity of other bodies.

What seems simple—a rock hurled through the air—suddenly requires a complex scientific explanation of how and why it acts as it does from launching until landing. If the rock were a meteor, a celestial body travelling through space, a variety of physical forces would act on it. Its trajectory would be affected by its velocity, the mass of other celestial bodies, and the distance between it and them.

But as a rock travelling through our atmosphere, which is not the near vacuum of space, this projectile is affected by the frictional drag of air and other aerodynamic effects, such as its weight-to-drag coefficient and the shape of its body. For projectiles like ballistic missiles, launched from earth to great heights for the purpose of striking a target at a distance, not only air resistance but the curvature and spin of Earth and the varying force of gravity at different altitudes are important factors. For relatively short distances at slower speeds than the 15,000 miles per hour at which huge military missiles travel, the earth may be considered flat and the force of gravity constant.

Bullets freely fired into the air are attracted by the earth's gravitational field. They are also slowed by aerodynamic forces such as atmosphere and weight and drag. These attractions cause the bullet to fall from the straight line path of aim provided by the launching mechanism. The rate of fall becomes greater near the target because the bullet falls faster and faster under the influences of gravity and the other forces reacting on it. Trajectories may be flattened when the overall speed of bullet travel is increased, because the length of time in which gravity and other forces have a chance to act is reduced.

The archer hunting with his bow is another example of the trajectory of a projectile. The force of trajectory of the arrow is slightly reduced when it departs from the bow because of the aerodynamic friction of air. At this point, it also becomes deflected by gravity. However, its momentum carries it to the target on a downward path toward the target rather than straight to the target. If gravity did not exist, it would head in a straight line toward the target—a straight line parallel to the ground, although toward the end of its flight

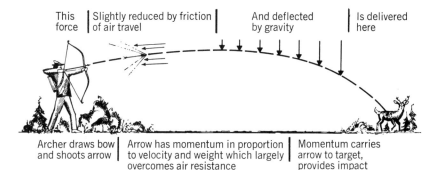

| This force | Slightly reduced by friction of air travel | And deflected by gravity | Is delivered here |

| Archer draws bow and shoots arrow | Arrow has momentum in proportion to velocity and weight which largely overcomes air resistance | Momentum carries arrow to target, provides impact |

Fig. 9-1.   Forces that determine the ballistic path.

it would again drop slightly from its path because its momentum would be slightly reduced by the aerodynamic effects of the atmosphere.

We know that the effects of gravity are predictable. No matter how much an object weighs, it will, of itself, fall no faster than necessary to cover a maximum vertical distance of 16 feet in its first second of fall. Given another second in which to be further speeded up by gravity, the object will fall an additional 48 feet. If a projectile is hurled straight upward, it will lose velocity due to the constant pull of the earth's gravity. The speed of the projectile moving upward will be reduced by gravity every second of flight. The free fall of a projectile begins, therefore, as soon as it is without the thrust or propulsive force applied to accelerate it.

In the development of a trajectory, a projectile must clear its own path through various gases comprising the blanket of air we live in. This creates pressures and frictions which tend to slow movement. The greatest air resistance a bullet or an artillery shell encounters is at its point of highest velocity—as it emerges from the muzzle of a gun. This resistance is a force which is at first aligned with the gun barrel. But as the path of the shell curves downward because of the effect of gravity, the apparent direction of resistance shifts to meet the changing angle of attack. The net overall effect is to shorten the trajectory or, if more elevation can be taken to

Trajectory if gravity and atmosphere did not exist

Effect of gravity and atmosphere on trajectory

Fig. 9-2. Trajectory of a projectile in the absence of a gravitational force compared to the trajectory when gravity is acting on it.

compensate, to somewhat increase flight time to the target. If it were possible to cut down air resistance in firing or launching the artillery shell in a near vacuum, the maximum range of the artillery projectile would increase considerably.

Objects moving through air meet an apparent wind which is of a strength proportional to the velocity at which the object is travelling. If the surface presented to this wind is broad or irregular, so that the air tends to pile up and be compressed, resistive forces are generated which will soon slow down the projectile. Streamlined objects, on the other hand, knife through the air so that little disturbance is created. The apparent frontal area of a projectile, as seen or struck head-on by air in its path, may thus be reduced by changing its shape or streamlining it even further. In fact, as speed is increased, streamlining becomes more necessary. Above the speed of sound compression effects cause the formation of a wedge-shaped shock front which only can be overcome by designing a projectile with an elongated nose sharpened to a point.

The earth is enclosed in concentric envelopes of various gases. Compressed by the weight of layers above, these gases tend to be more dense at the lower levels closer to earth. The comparative absence of air in the upper stratosphere and ionosphere aids the flight of ballistic missiles by offering little resistance to passage. The shock produced when the missile hits dense air, and the heating of the skin or surface of the missile because of friction, are problems encountered when a ballistic projectile dives steeply at supersonic speed into the lower atmosphere.

In effect, the guidance of crude or basic projectiles is therefore dependent upon propulsion which lifts the missile to its trajectory, from which it "falls" to its target. The modern, solid propellant rockets are not much different in principle from those invented more than 700 years ago by the Chinese.

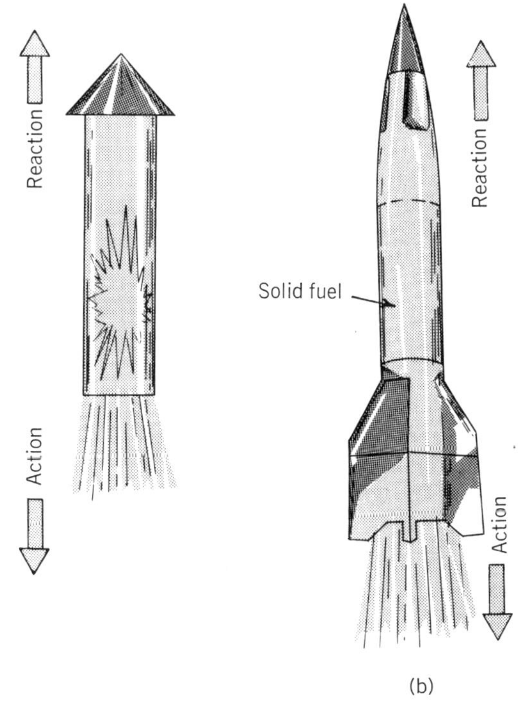

Fig. 9-3. (a) The solid propellant packed in this primitive sky rocket burns in the same manner as (b) the solid propellant in this modern missile. Both propellants burn at a constant, steady rate. Exhaust gases provide the thrust which propels these projectiles. If there were no exhaust outlet, the propellant would react as an explosive, bursting through the container rather than burning steadily with a constant flow of energy to push the container in one direction.

(b)

The propellant is solidly packed into the case of the rocket and the duration of burning and cutoff of rocket power then determines its flight path and trajectory. Its range, however, is dependent upon the factors of thrust and weight. The same is true for the liquid-fueled rocket.

Take the case of a missile. When it is launched vertically, the rocket engine must develop sufficient thrust to lift the missile straight up. The launching of a missile weighing 10,000 pounds consisting of fuel and structure requires a thrust equal to the weight of the missile to oppose the force of gravity (g). Sufficient acceleration for the missile to depart on a ballistic trajectory requires additional thrust caused by a steady burning of the fuel. A thrust of 14,999 pounds will at first provide a margin of 4,000 pounds of lift to produce an upward acceleration equivalent to one half g. Such a thrust will lift a 10,000-pound missile about eight feet off the launching pad in one second. Thus the rate of acceleration, with constant thrust, will reach one g when the missile has been lightened to 7,500 pounds by consumption of its propellant.

During this powered phase in launching and subsequent flight, the thrust of the rocket engine overcomes both gravity and air resistance. The missile is made to climb steeply at first in order to reach thinner air as quickly as possible, because air is denser at lower levels and, moreover, is likely to be somewhat turbulent. Gradually the missile tilts from the vertical, according to a preset program, so that it steers itself into a great arc terminating at its target.

The moment of transition from powered flight to ballistic flight comes when rocket power is cut off and the missile is free to fall. This event is comparable to that occurring when a shell leaves the barrel of a gun which has guided it and has provided a set angle of departure and direction of ballistic flight. The rocket-powered ballistic missile, steered or guided in powered flight until its path coincides with the intended ballistic trajectory, will follow that ballistic trajectory in free fall flight—without further need for rocket thrust. When accuracy of impact on a target is desired at the termination of ballistic flight, no further rocket thrust should be applied

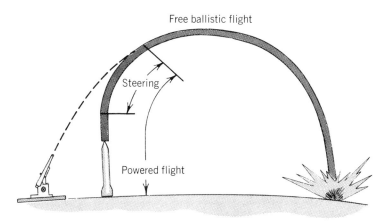

Free ballistic flight

Steering

Powered flight

Fig. 9-4. After the thrust of the rocket engine overcomes both gravity and air resistance and then shuts off, the missile is free to fall to its target in the same way that a shell fired from an artillery piece falls to its target in what is known as free ballistic flight.

beyond a certain point, or the missile will overshoot the target. Similarly, if rocket power is cut off too soon, the missile will strike short of the target, though a timer may be used to preset the length of time that the rocket engine will deliver thrust, thus giving the missile greater accuracy.

The missile components are also important to the control and guidance of the rocket. Actually, the size of these components determines the size of the entire missile. Its size, therefore, is a fair indication of its ability to carry a payload and a large supply of propellants to provide extended burning time and a longer range. Propellant tanks will normally be located directly forward of the rocket engine. If the thrust unit is to be jettisoned (dropped off) after cutoff of rocket power, the point of separation between the delivery unit and its thrust unit is logically just forward of the propellant tanks. The payload is located in or near the nose to place the center of gravity well forward for good stability in ballistic flight. Instruments are placed directly back of the payload. The instruments can then accompany the ballistic payload on its trip to the target in order to provide last-minute terminal guidance for improved accuracy.

A ballistic missile heavily loaded with rocket fuel rises slowly from the launching pad. Lift-off is a critical period. At first, very little steering is obtainable through aerodynamic control surfaces because such surfaces require considerable forward velocity and flow of air over them to be effective. To obtain all necessary steering and stability for the missile during lift-off, the direction of the whole rocket stream or thrust may be adjusted by tilting the rocket engine which is mounted on flexible supports within the tail. This tilting action brings about steering corrections in attitude whenever the apparent wind, created by the rocket's forward motion, strikes the side of one or more fins.

In later-model missiles smaller vernier rockets, tiny jet engines mounted on gimbals, maintained the correct course during launching and flight along the programmed path of the missile. However, the main booster engine provided the necessary lift-off thrust to push the rocket away from

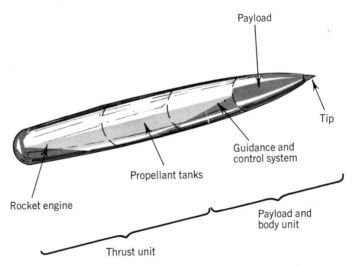

Fig. 9-5.   Location of rocket components.

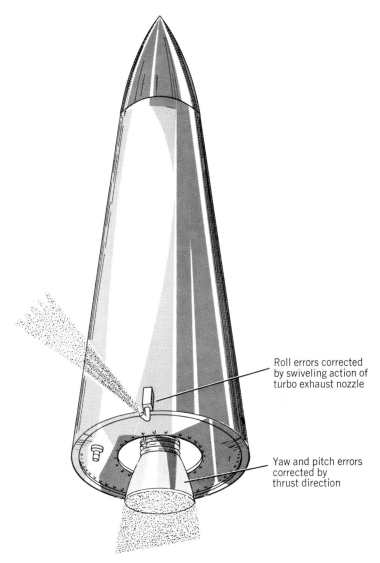

Roll errors corrected
by swiveling action of
turbo exhaust nozzle

Yaw and pitch errors
corrected by
thrust direction

Fig. 9-6.   In missiles equipped with gimbaled engines, yaw and pitch
attitude errors are corrected by thrust direction control, which is
achieved when the thrust chamber of the rocket engine is swiveled.
Roll errors are corrected by the swiveling action of the exhaust nozzle.

earth. The next sequence follows the cut-off of rocket power. At this point the ballistic missile coasts upward into thinner and thinner air. Since control by air vane or rudder becomes more and more impractical at higher altitudes without an aid stream, the most that can be done is to keep the nose pointed in the direction of travel so that the attitude of the missile at re-entry will be correct. This control of attitude in the near-vacuum of the ionosphere is obtained by means of spatial jet nozzles located at the rear of the payload. These jets, emitting a stream of gas under pressure, rotate the payload much like a bullet or artillery shell leaving a rifled barrel. Thus, the payload rotates about its own center of gravity and the necessary attitude correction is supplied.

Current working models of missile and spacecraft boosters are equipped with the gimbaled vernier rocket motors along

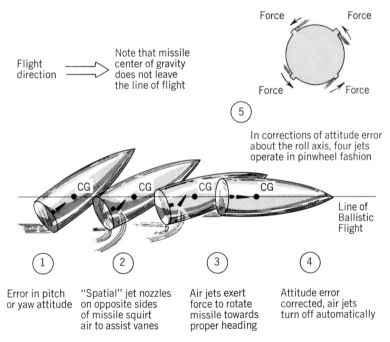

Flight direction

Note that missile center of gravity does not leave the line of flight

Force   Force

Force   Force

⑤

In corrections of attitude error about the roll axis, four jets operate in pinwheel fashion

CG   CG   CG   CG

Line of Ballistic Flight

①   ②   ③   ④

Error in pitch or yaw attitude

"Spatial" jet nozzles on opposite sides of missile squirt air to assist vanes

Air jets exert force to rotate missile towards proper heading

Attitude error corrected, air jets turn off automatically

Fig. 9-7.   Control in the upper atmosphere.

with gimbaled main engines which correct yaw and pitch attitude errors by thrust direction control. This is achieved when the thrust chamber of the rocket engine is swiveled by hydraulic actuators. Roll errors are corrected by the hydraulically controlled swiveling action of the vernier motors that are slightly outboard along the base of the booster.

Coupled to the inertial guidance system, the swiveling rocket engines automatically move in whatever direction is necessary to provide the direction of thrust required to keep the missile on course during its critical lift-off period. Early model military missiles were guided on lift-off from the ground. However, the development of inertial guidance for these missiles put within the rocket an entirely self-contained control unit which did not depend upon outside instructions. Computers within the guidance system require, for insertion of time and distance values, that the exact geographical locations of both the launch site and the target be known. Preset instructions furnished for playback during flight will tilt the missile forward so that its path emerges into the desired ballistic trajectory. The motion-measuring accelerometers, carried within the guidance system located on a space-oriented stable platform, keep track of velocity changes and continuously supply this velocity information to guidance computers.

From this information, the guidance computers can, by the mechanical process involving time, derive distance error data. Thus inertial guidance will enable the correction of any drift during powered flight and the computation of the exact moment for rocket power cut off. The computer then will remember displacement errors occurring in free ballistic flight, after the engines have been shut down, and automatically correct the dive angle in a brief period of terminal guidance following re-entry into dense atmosphere over the target.

Today, of course, the techniques of launching rocket-powered spacecraft have improved considerably, so that the exact techniques developed since the first missiles and satellites were launched in the late 1950s now make it possible in most cases to insert these space vehicles in perfectly programmed orbits and trajectories.

As we have seen, the development of military missiles has given scientists the experience and knowhow to build the more complex manned and unmanned spacecraft that are constantly orbiting the earth. Many guidance and control systems have been developed for the military weapons. The best features of these systems have been incorporated in those in use now. Here are some of those early systems:

Command Guidance. Provided for the reception and execution of commands originating outside the missile. These are based on knowledge of the missile's motion and position relative to the target.

Direction Along a Beam. Accomplished similar results as Command Guidance. The missile is equipped with the necessary electronics to keep it automatically in the center of a radar or radio beam. Command function, or changing the missile flight path, may be exercised by moving the beam in space while the missile is in motion.

Navigational Net Direction. Achieved by using one of the different forms of radio navigation to lead the missile to a point which bears some relation to a navigational net. This can be preset to coincide with the target. One such type of "navnet" is LORAN which we discussed in an earlier chapter. The sending stations of the LORAN "navnet" provide the signals which control the missile's flight path.

Homing Devices and Seekers. Homing guidance and control is furnished the missile by placing within it a form of automatic seeker sensitive to one particular type of energy. In such a case, the missile is directed to its target by energy radiated by its objective. Some of the air-to-air, air-to-ground and ground-to-air missiles like the Sidewinder, Hawk and Nike family consist of *Heat-Seekers, Light-Seekers,* and *Radar-Seekers.*

The *heat-seeking missile* is, by its very name, highly sensitive to heat. It can chase up the tailpipe of a jet fighter or bomber, or fly to targets like factories which give off heat from smokestacks or utilize heat in the manufacturing process. The missile homes-in on the target which gives off the greatest amount of unshielded temperature.

The *light-seeking missile* contains an instrument highly sensitive to brightness. The infra-red light thrown off by heat is another case in point. A light-seeking missile designed to home-in on infra-red seeks out a particular variation of light. The *radar-seeker* utilizes two operational methods. A radar-sensitive instrument may be installed in the nose to "home" the missile on an enemy radar station. The target also may be illuminated by radar and the missile homes in on the radar echoes reflecting off the target.

Many new developments are constantly being researched, to provide the best possible guidance and control system available to place spacecraft accurately on course. We will note some of these more refined systems in the chapters to follow.

10

Project Mercury

The Mercury man-in-space program is now "ancient" history when we try to chronicle the Space Age. But Project Mercury proved that man could function in a spacecraft travelling through a new frontier. In fact, everything about the Mercury-Atlas spacecraft and booster represented all of the science and technological knowledge that man had accumulated over the centuries. We now see how this knowledge was used in a manned spacecraft.

At 9:47 a.m., February 20, 1962, two brilliant lances of fire spit from the flanks of Atlas 109-D2, 93-foot rocket booster with Mercury spacecraft and escape rigging attached. This giant snarled and rumbled into life. From her belly, a volcano of flame suddenly gushed downward and the giant strained to break free of the shackles which held her to the launching pad. The clamps held fast as the booster built up the all-important thrust power that is required to lift her into the heavens.

High above the fiery cascade, Astronaut John H. Glenn, Jr., heard the swelling rumble of rocket thunder and his body responded to the vibrations that swept upward from the Atlas booster. His eyes scanned the instrument panel and his hand firmly grasped the "chicken switch," the safety control that would send him rocketing away from a disabled or exploding booster and return him safely to earth. A pall of white smoke and steam blanketed launch complex 14. In the control center half a mile away, all instruments registered green—GO! The volcano was in full cry, and the Atlas thrust back at the earth with all the energy her engineers had imparted to her rounded flanks. The instruments were satisfied; they responded with an electronic nod, a spurt of current and a command.

Fig. 10-1.   Low-angle view of Atlas and Friendship 7 spacecraft between gantry equipment during prelaunch preparations. (NASA)

The steel shackles flew back and Atlas 109-D with her
human passenger was free. Spilling golden flame and violet

Fig. 10-2. Mercury-Atlas 6 lifting John H. Glenn, Jr. in Friendship 7 spacecraft to begin a three-orbit journey around the earth. (NASA)

plumes downward, the giant rejected the earth once enough thrust had been built up during the first seconds after ignition.

Slowly, then faster, she began to rush away from the planet that spawned her.

"The clock is operating," Astronaut Glenn reported. From this moment on, time—real or actual time—would become an important factor throughout the flight of the spacecraft "Friendship 7."

Here is the sequence of events in the control and guidance of the Atlas booster:

As the booster engines ignite and the Atlas lifts from its pad, the rocket is guided for about two minutes by an internal autopilot. Then, radars "lock on" to the rising Atlas and signals are fed to the computer.

Once the radar link is established, the computer can give orders. The first command is "BECO"—booster engine cut-off and jettisoning of the booster assembly and protective skirts. The rocket continues to rise, powered by only its sustainer engine. The computer accepts flight reports from the Atlas transmitted along the radar path, compares this information with a preplanned set of conditions, then calculates corrections and sends them back to the Atlas along a second radar path.

The commands alter the yaw and pitch of the rocket, fishtailing it gently onto its desired course. As optimum trajectory is approached, the Atlas responds to final, fine corrections and nears what John Glenn later called "the window," the point in space the rocket must pass through to achieve proper orbit conditions.

During the ground guidance phase, plotting devices on the computer trace a graphic record of pitch and yaw error, flight path angle, yaw velocity, altitude and rocket velocity. When corrections have been made and all pre-planned conditions met, it is mathematically certain the spacecraft will go into orbit.

Three hundred seconds later, exactly on schedule, a number of things happen. The surface of our planet lies a shade more than 100 miles below, and the Atlas, which originally weighed 250,000 pounds fully loaded with fuel, metal parts and assemblies, has now changed her weight. At 5,000 degrees

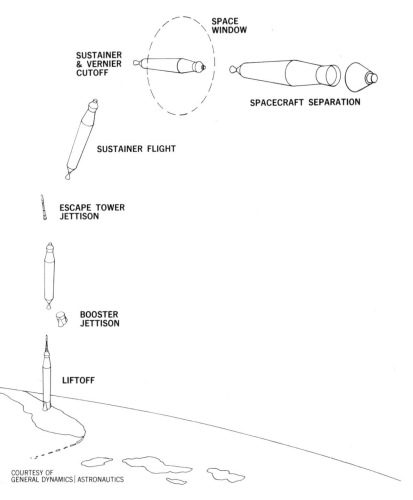

SPACE
WINDOW

SUSTAINER
& VERNIER
CUTOFF

SPACECRAFT SEPARATION

SUSTAINER FLIGHT

ESCAPE TOWER
JETTISON

BOOSTER
JETTISON

LIFTOFF

COURTESY OF
GENERAL DYNAMICS | ASTRONAUTICS

Fig. 10-3.   Stages in the launching of a spacecraft. (General Dy-
namics/Astronautics)

temperature, her combustion chambers drained the superfine
kerosene and supercold liquid oxygen that filled her steel
tanks. The three mighty rocket engines have ejected the propellant fuel in a continuing stream of blazing gases.

The velocity of the booster and spacecraft is impressive. No longer does she point vertically into the sky; now she rushes horizontally above the surface in a ballistic trajectory that is an orbit around the earth—an orbit that over a period of days would dissolve into a fiery trajectory back to earth if the law of gravity was permitted to exert its natural pull on the spacecraft and booster. In the case of the Atlas booster, however, gravity does assert itself and pull the booster back to earth.

Precisely at 100.3 miles above the earth's surface, the mighty Atlas and her spacecraft is on the edge of the aerothermodynamic border of earth's atmosphere. Considering all the factors of velocity and height, and the density of the few remaining gases that thrust this above earth, this is the edge of true space. And all of this happens in 300 seconds.

Now the sequence of events continues. Explosive bolts crack hard; their sound booms with a hollow roar in the cavernous emptied tanks of the Atlas booster. Blue-white gases from the bolts sever clamp rings and metal connections and spring them free. Exactly one more second passes. Three small rockets at the base of the bell-shaped Mercury spacecraft fire. Flame lances in the vacuum of space. Everything that is happening is precise and mathematical. The three rockets are called posigrades and their plasticized solid fuel burns with a measured thrust of 1,250 pounds—pushing the shingle-sided spacecraft away from the booster. The two objects separate with a speed of 24 feet per second; they will continue to drift apart, not only in speed but in destiny. The booster will end up in a fiery mass in its plunge back to earth.

For if the mathematics of spaceflight continues to be precise, and an exhaustively computed schedule is maintained down to the exact second, the capsule will return safely after three orbits around the world. Atlas 109-D, however, can be considered debris. Her stainless steel sides reflect brilliantly in the morning sun of space. Her lines are beautiful. Her mass in orbit only a few years past would have represented a staggering feat. Now she's doomed to incineration when gravity begins to reclaim her bulk. The atmosphere that sustains life on the earth's surface is hostile to a five-ton mass plunging from space at 300 miles a minute. The meeting of Atlas 109-D and the thickening atmosphere will produce the inevitable. There will be friction, a temperature of many thousands of degrees and a fiery end as molten pieces of metal strike the earth.

As for the spacecraft, its posigrade rockets give "Friendship 7" and its passenger—now weighing a total of 2,987 pounds—enough of a kick to increase its velocity by 50 feet per second. Astronaut John Glenn is aware of all of these physical and technical facts that have placed him in orbit. But the precise meaning is of greater interest to the men in Mercury Control, the ground control center which can maneuver the spacecraft and its passenger by flashing signals into space.

The orbital path has now been achieved by split-second programming of the launch vehicle staging, velocity, pitchover (turnabout), yaw control and engine cutoff. The Atlas booster had accelerated continuously during its powered flight, arrived at the insertion point travelling at a precise speed, and completed its pitchover to an earth-referenced horizontal path with the spacecraft's longitudinal axis in an exact attitude at the same moment it reached that orbital point.

To direct the spacecraft into its orbital flight position is an electronic brain with sensitivity so great that it can measure the mass of a human hair. The brain senses—with the help of an inertial guidance system—the movement of the spacecraft, specifically its attitude. Electronic commands open valves, hydrogen peroxide, stored under pressure, snakes through the fuel lines and burst in carefully-measured proportion and quantity from nozzles that are exposed to space.

This force exerted by the gas—which in the silence and emptiness of space makes not even a sound outside the capsule—is negligible. After all, the conditions of space and orbit are totally alien to those of the earth. The spacecraft no longer has any weight. It is falling around the earth. However, it has a specific mass, and the thrust of the jet nozzles is enough to swing the spacecraft around to its orbital attitude.

"Friendship 7" does a half-turn. Where the astronaut inside was facing in the direction of the flight, he now faces backwards. The capsule tilts in response to its jets. Using the horizon far below as a reference line, "Friendship 7" tilts exactly 34 degrees above the horizon. The astronaut is now hurtling through space at nearly five miles per second, almost 300 miles per minute and 17,544.1 miles per hour. He's seated backwards so that he can see where he has been.

From the astronaut's point of view, the Mercury spacecraft is an engineering miracle, although a contraption. For the Mercury Project is just the flivver stage of space flight development. The bell-shaped Mercury spacecraft, nine and a half

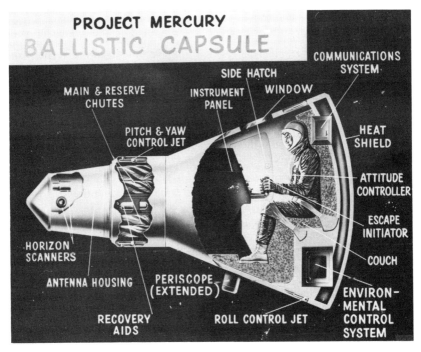

Fig. 10-4. Manned Mercury spacecraft (with cutaway view of interior). (NASA)

feet high, and six feet wide at its broadest base, has an interior about the size of a telephone booth, with equipment, dials, meters, controls, power devices and a thousand other items jammed into every available cubic inch of space.

On a console to the left, as well as in the center, are the navigational and control instruments. The astronaut also has his optical viewer for his periscope, which protrudes from the spacecraft when it's in orbit. On the right section of the main panel are environmental system gauges and controls, a battery of electrical switches, instrument dials and meters, and an elaborate radio communications system. Altogether, the Mercury spacecraft has well over 100 lights, fuses, switches, varying controls and display facilities.

Squeezed neatly beneath the instrument panel and controls is the astronaut's couch of crushable honeycomb material, bonded to a fiberglass shell and lined with rubber padding. Safety straps and harnesses are attached.

The Mercury spacecraft is controlled by 18 different reaction-thrust nozzles located about the surface of the vehicle. From fuel tanks within the spacecraft, hydrogen peroxide is used to create steam (pressure) of specifically measured thrust, which controls the desired flight or orbital attitudes. Some of these thrust nozzles fire only one pound of thrust, others as much as 24 pounds.

The Mercury is a complicated system with a host of control problems to resolve—attitude in orbit, attitude during the moment of firing the retrorockets for re-entry and subsequent landing, damping out oscillations during the critical re-entry maneuver and recovery from tumbling maneuvers. In orbit, as we have seen, the spacecraft is weightless and likely to wander about on its three axes—pitch (up and down), yaw (side to side), and roll (like an airplane in level flight but rolling its wings around and around). Space flight snarls these normally complicated control problems by introducing the possibility of tumbling—the simultaneous movement of the spacecraft through all three axes.

In order to maintain attitude control through this regime of flight, an automatic pilot in the spacecraft is programmed beforehand, to go through the necessary maneuvers to retain desired attitudes. This isn't enough, however. The astronaut also has three manual attitude-control systems. A "fly-by-wire" arrangement allows him to control the spacecraft attitude by providing a direct override linkage through the automatic pilot. There also is a direct manual system which works through mechanical linkages to the manual-control fuel system, and a rate-command system which also uses the manual fuel system.

These manual systems are motivated by a control stick, much like that of a fighter airplane; the stick creates the desired effect of attitude control by causing the jet nozzles outside the spacecraft to discharge their hydrogen-peroxide gas, or thrust. When the astronaut moves the stick back and forth, he exercises movement in pitch. When he moves the stick from side to side, he has roll control. Both of these maneuvers follow the control movements of those in an airplane. Rotating the stick adds a yaw control for sideways motion which is not paralleled in aircraft. In aircraft, the pilot used rudder controls, operated by foot pressure, to attain yaw.

The actual Mercury control system consists of five gyroscopes, a tiny accelerometer and a small computer. Together, these components are known formally as the ASCS—Attitude Stabilization and Control System.

The ASCS, in concert with other systems aboard the spacecraft, is capable of automatically taking a Mercury astronaut from his insertion into orbit, all the way through his planned mission and reentry phase without any effort on his part. In addition, a semi-automatic mode (fly-by-wire) and a manual control mode are provided.

The ASCS automatically points the Mercury spacecraft in the proper direction after separation from the Atlas booster. The gyros sense spacecraft attitude and any tendency it may have to twist and turn in one direction or another. The computer compares signals from the gyros to pre-programmed directions, which tell it how the spacecraft is supposed to be oriented and sends appropriate commands to reaction jets to make corrections.

The ASCS is programmed to arrest within five seconds any tumbling effect induced at the moment of separation from the launch vehicle.

After those five seconds, another automatic command is issued to swing the Mercury 180 degrees so that its blunt end is forward. The other end is tilted down to the retrograde attitude, from which an immediate reentry can be initiated if necessary.

With the initial orientation completed, the astronaut is free to take over. An attitude and rate indicated system located on the control panel gives him a visual presentation of the roll, pitch and yaw conditions.

Astronaut control may be retained until the time for reentry approaches. At this point, the automatic system will normally be actuated to assure the precise control necessary for assuming the best retrograde and reentry attitudes.

Following pre-programmed instructions, the ASCS first tilts the blunt end up (34 degrees from horizontal) to the proper position for retrograde rocket firing. After the retro-rockets slow the spacecraft for reentry, the control system repositions the spacecraft with the blunt end tilted down slightly (1.5 degrees).

At about 300,000 feet, atmospheric drag begins to build up. When it reaches a force equal to five-hundredths of earth's gravitational force, the tiny accelerometer in the control system sends a signal which starts the spacecraft rolling at slightly less than two revolutions per minute.

The roll distributes the heat of reentry over the full surface of the heat shield and increases landing accuracy. At approximately 20,000 feet, a drogue parachute is released, and at 10,000 feet the main landing chute is released, lowering the spacecraft to its final ocean landing.

We can see just how complex the control and guidance of spacecraft is for the astronaut under zero gravity conditions. It demands extraordinary practice, then countless hours of more practice.

On the other hand, a great deal of practice went into the Mercury Control phase of spaceflight. An entirely automatic and ground controlled and automatic control system was installed in the Mercury spacecraft. If something went wrong in the spacecraft itself, so that it would not respond to the controls in the astronaut's hands, then the logical step would be to have a backup system controlled from the ground. In a paper entitled "A Review of Knowledge Acquired from the First Manned Satellite Program," Christopher Kraft, Jr., the man in charge at Mercury Control, reported the following information:

". . . part of the design philosophy, and perhaps the most important one in regard to future systems, is the automatic systems contained in the Mercury spacecraft. When the project started, we had no definitive information on how man would react in the spacecraft system. To insure that we returned the spacecraft to earth as planned, the critical functions would have to be automatic. The control system would keep the spacecraft stabilized at precisely 34 degrees above the horizontal. The retrorockets would be fired by an automatic sequence under a programmed or ground command . . . The Mercury vehicle was a highly automatic system and the man essentially was riding along as a passenger and observer."

This paper also described how the two unmanned Mercury-Atlas flights prior to Astronaut Glenn's MA-6 mission of three orbits around the world were the most difficult of the orbital flights. "They had to be flown using only one automatic control system," the report continued. "We had no man along with the ability to override or correct malfunctions in the systems. One of the flights ended prematurely due to malfunctions that we could not correct from the ground. In both cases, a man could have assumed manual control and continued the flight for the full number of orbits. It is no hypothesis or theory; it has been borne out by the facts. With this design criteria in mind, the Cooper (MA-9) flight was a fitting climax to the Mercury program. Not only did it yield new information for other spacecraft programs, but it demonstrated that man had a unique capability to rescue a mission that would not have been successfully completed with the automatic equipment provided.

"As we move into the Gemini and Apollo programs, a maneuvering capability has been built into the spacecraft to allow changes in flight path, both while in orbit and during reentry into the atmosphere."

But future improvements in guidance and control are only possible from past experience. One such experience was that of Astronaut M. Scott Carpenter in his MA-7 mission on May 24, 1962. In what was a virtual carbon copy of Astronaut Glenn's three orbits of the earth, with the exception of some additional experiments and maneuvers, Carpenter's maximum speed was 17,548.6 miles per hour when he fired his retrorockets. However, the attitude of his spacecraft "Aurora 7" was off the 34-degree angle from the horizon. There was a 25-degree yaw error at the time the retrorockets were fired to slow his spacecraft for its reentry through the atmosphere and descent to earth. His landing occurred 250 miles beyond the predicted impact point as a result of this error.

MA-9, the final flight in the Mercury program, was launched on May 15, 1963, with Astronaut L. Gordon Cooper, Jr., who orbited the earth for more than a day in this "Faith 7" spacecraft, which attained a maximum speed of 17,546.6 miles per hour. One of the prime control and guidance experiments was allowing drifting flight. This was developed to save electrical power and hydrogen-peroxide fuel and to permit the astronaut time for other activities. In this mode of flight, the astronaut first obtained the required spacecraft attitudes and then powered down.

In space, there is no *up* and no *down*. However, inertial guidance systems worked sufficiently well to keep the spacecraft in a constant right-side-up position in relation to the earth below.

On earth was the ground control system that could duplicate any maneuvers the astronaut could perform. We shall now see why ground control was important in the Mercury program when Americans were taking their first flights into space. Throughout any flight through space, especially experimental flights, it is necessary that physiological data on the astronaut, environmental data inside his spacecraft, and en-

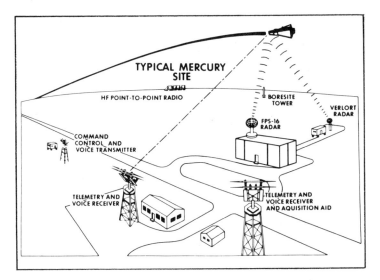

Fig. 10-5. Project Mercury communications and telemetry.

gineering data about the performance of the spacecraft during its flight must be acquired, instantly displayed and recorded for future use. The acquisition and use of this data permit the technical and control staff to operate as the central world operations control point throughout the flight.

Technical data—the parameters of performance—was fed to Mercury Control from the spacecraft by telemetry—the science of measuring a quantity, transmitting the measured value of this quantity by radio to a distant station, where it is translated into jargon that can be simultaneously interpreted and recorded by scientists and technicians while the measurements are occurring. All of the Mercury spacecraft were fitted out with a small three-pound black box called a commutator, which selected the series of constant technical data for which the vehicle was wired. Acting like a traffic cop, the commutator fed select information to on-board telemetry transmitters which sent the data back to earth. Specifically, the telemetry systems answered the question: Are the spacecraft systems functioning?

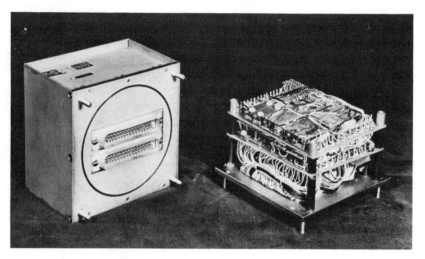

Fig. 10-6. Two views of 316 telemetry commutator used aboard Mercury spacecraft. (Applied Electronics Corporation of New Jersey)

As the spacecraft orbited the earth, telemetered data was received in Mercury Control, a 50- by 60-foot sprawling enclosure where men and electronics merged in a strange and wonderful team. Displayed on four flight recorders was the vital information. Recorder Number One plotted the launch path as gamma (inertial flight path angle) versus velocity ratio, and the orbital path as altitude above spherical earth versus velocity. Recorder Number Two plotted the launch path as cross range deviation and altitude versus range, and the orbital path as semi-major axis deviation and altitude versus ground elapsed time. Recorder Number Three plotted insertion velocity and longitudinal acceleration versus elapsed time, and yaw error and insertion altitude versus time-to-go-to-sustainer-engine cutoff, and the orbit as earth-fixed longitude or perigee, and eccentricity versus elapsed time. Recorder Number Four plotted a chart of the launch recovery area. One pen plotted the landing point if the retrorockets were fired immediately before tower separation, and also the landing point if the retrorockets were fired in 30 seconds. The second pen plotted the landing point for a delayed retrofire after the spacecraft reached a prescribed altitude.

We now can see that the mathematics of spaceflight is an involved process requiring computers to analyze this type of data in seconds and come up with answers that would take men hours, days and weeks to work out with conventional slide rules, reams of paper, scores of pencils—and time.

Thanks to telemetry and high-speed computers, no matter what happens with the spacecraft during the booster phase of flight, during insertion into orbit, or during orbit, the flight recorders in Mercury Control were able to display instantly and exactly what was happening at any given moment and, given a prescribed situation, what would happen. It's almost as if the men in ground control could "see" the spacecraft. Actually, the situation is similar to driving a car on a fast, curving slippery road. What will happen, for example, if the brakes are jammed on at exactly 63.7 miles per hour while entering a turn with a side-acceleration factor of so many percentages over the force of one gravity? How far will the auto skid? When will the skid begin? Where will the car stop? What will happen during every instant of the future time period?

This is the kind of information translated into space flight data that is instantly answered for the flight display systems in ground control. The brain center for answering questions is the Goddard Space Flight Center in Maryland, a strange miracle of a space-age operation. Built into the Center's computers are special information channels that permit the actual space flight mission to be measured on a real-time basis—as it is actually happening. This allows ground control personnel to see their information displayed on the basis of not what happened several minutes earlier, but what is happening at the present and what will happen in the immediate future.

The "critical" time elements of space flight include the launch and the moment of insertion of the spacecraft into its orbit. The later critical moments concern reentry, starting at the time when ground control decides that it's time to return to earth. For future space missions, the critical periods will

Fig. 10-7.   Mercury-Atlas 9 leaves Pad 14 at Cape Kennedy with astronaut L. Gordon Cooper aboard for the longest manned orbital flight to date. (NASA)

cover rendezvous in space and landings and launchings from the moon and other planets. An example of how the brain center operates on a real time basis can best be described by the MA-9 manned flight.

From the moment the Atlas booster left the launch stand to begin ascent, the computers at the Goddard Space Flight Center instantly moved onto a preprogrammed operational basis. The mechanics of the flight had been programmed into the computer operation to take into consideration not merely the events that were scheduled, but also any possible combination of events that could occur in the event of a malfunction. The moment the booster had its first motion, the computers began operating on a real-time basis. They received information from the spacecraft as well as the booster. The booster information consisted of the operation of its accelerometers, attitude indicators, and other performance-reading instruments that provided a complete running flight picture measured down to a tolerance of one half-second.

This is the information that flowed to Mercury Control and was instantly relayed to Goddard. The flight-performance readings continued on their way to Maryland until the moment that the sustainer engine—the Atlas booster's main engine—shut down, ending the powered flight. The next measured sequence included separating the clamps that held the spacecraft to the Atlas booster, and then the firing of the posigrade rockets that pushed the spacecraft away from the inert booster and initiated turnaround.

All of this occurred automatically, and within seconds after it happened, it was displayed at ground control. Then came the 30-second critical period after spacecraft separation from the booster. During the period of half a minute, the Goddard computers had to digest the final bits of data on the booster phase of the flight. They had to make—still within this 30-second period—a positive *Go* or *No Go* recommendation to continue the flight. These computers displayed at Goddard and simultaneously at Mercury Control the data that revealed whether or not the spacecraft was in orbit, or if it would reenter the atmosphere before a complete orbit was achieved.

If the reading indicated that the spacecraft had not been inserted properly into orbit, then ground control would have had to decide instantly to fire the retrorockets so that the vehicle would reenter in a preselected "abort recovery zone." Otherwise, the astronaut might have plunged down from space to land in the midst of jungle, mountains, or in an ocean area far from any immediate recovery.

During the actual flight, real-time can be utilized, but it's rarely needed. However, the end of the mission then becomes the next critical phase. When the spacecraft approached the end of its final orbit and was ready to begin reentry operations, the computers again snapped into real-time immediacy basis. If ground control had to know what would happen if the retrorockets fired at any given instant, the computers would display instantly the exact position where the spacecraft would land.

Everything was taken into consideration by the computers —point of entry, atmospheric conditions, sea conditions and literally everything else that might affect the spacecraft. One great big ball of wax, so to speak, was pushed into the computer banks which in turn cranked out every possible situation to be studied; these situations form the basis for which rapid decisions might have had to be made. In other words, the computer can be thought of as a digester of problems and a destroyer of question marks. During a flight, while the computers were idling, they always checked back, reporting every few minutes what a predicted impact point would be if the retros should accidently fire at any given moment before the originally programmed time to return to earth.

The Mercury space flights were nothing more than experimental and paved the way for the more complex and sophisticated guidance and control systems in Gemini and Apollo spacecraft.

11

Project Gemini

Slowly the spacecraft drifts toward the unmanned satellite. Brief bursts of power from the manned spacecraft thrusts it closer and closer. Now the critical moment is at hand. The two astronauts manipulate their power controls rapidly, surely, carefully. The manned spacecraft eases slowly but smoothly into an adapter extending from the unmanned satellite. Contact is made. Again the reaction jets spurt power. The contact now is more certain. Then it is secure. The manned spacecraft and the unmanned satellite are latched together, a solid joining.

The two have been "docked in orbit." The astronauts confirm the connections between the two space vehicles. Far below on earth, the computers are still hard at work digesting the new information. Data are telemetered through space to the manned spacecraft, now in command of the satellite. Reaction jets spurt their gases, and the attitude changes once again. Now a heavier mass is moving through space—the two vehicles joined together. Then the astronauts count down in their spacecraft. One man closes a switch. The engine in the satellite flames into life once more burning steadily. When it cuts off, the double-spacecraft system is moving faster than before. It is in a new orbit with a perigee higher than first achieved.

For the next several hours the astronauts practice different maneuvers in space. Then it is time to try a new phase. A hatch over the cockpit opens and one of the astronauts slowly pulls himself out and floats close to the spacecraft, anchored to it by a safety line.

During a period of two weeks these two astronauts live in space, until word comes from ground control that it's time to return to earth. Working as a team, they check out their

Fig. 11-1. Artist's concept of a rendezvous achieved by the Gemini spacecraft and the Agena vehicle. At nearly identical orbital velocities they are latched together utilizing visual observation to provide steering for final clocking. (NASA)

instrument panels. Lights flash on the consoles, switches are opened and closed. The locking device holding the two satellites together is released. The manned spacecraft eases away slowly from the unmanned satellite. A brief burst of power from the spacecraft, and the two vehicles begin to drift farther apart, in separate diverging orbits.

Gemini is on its way home.

This, in brief, sums up the Gemini spacecraft—the program that is another step nearer to a landing on the moon. Project Gemini is named for the twin stars, Castor and Pollux. Its name aptly describes its mission—the orbiting of two men in a single spaceship. Space scientists refer to Gemini as "the bridge." They explain that Gemini bridges the gap between the one-man Mercury spacecraft and the three-man Apollo spaceship.

Perhaps the most important phase of the Gemini program is the development of rendezvous techniques in space. As we have seen in earlier chapters, spacecraft travelling from earth to another planet—or even to an orbiting space station—will not be launched and aimed at the target. Instead, future spacecraft will maneuver in flight so as to meet or rendezvous in space with their destination.

To put it another way, the earlier Mercury spacecraft had a *control* system. Gemini, the next step in space flight, has *guidance* and *control*. The difference between the two is really a comparison of capability. Envision the Mercury and Gemini spacecraft as a pair of swivel chairs. One is bolted to the floor and swivels. The other swivel chair is mounted on castors. Mercury astronauts could twist, turn and tip their spacecraft, but they were confined to one orbit, like the bolted chair confined to its stationary position on the floor. Gemini astronauts also will be able to twist, turn and tip their spacecraft; in addition they will have the capability to move to a new location in space just as the chair on castors may be pushed across the floor to a new position.

The difference between Gemini and Mercury space flights may also be described as somewhat like the difference between travelling by train and by car. Mercury has always

Fig. 11-2. Artist's conception of the rendezvous and docking maneuver in space when the two-man Gemini spacecraft mates with the
Agena target vehicle.

been restricted to its single orbital "track" like a train, while Gemini offers a selection of space "highways" to choose from. The terms for these individual freedoms of movment are rotational and translational, the former referring to movement about the three axes of a fixed body (pitch, roll and yaw), the latter to movement from one position in space to another. Mercury spacecraft had no need for guidance because, in a manner of speaking, they were not going anywhere except where they were aimed. They were launched into orbit just as a bullet is shot from a gun. Like a bullet, they kept going until they lost speed with a burst of retrorocket power and fell back to earth. Despite the single orbit of the Mercury spacecraft, it could be twisted, turned, tipped and tilted during its long free-fall around the earth; this is what "control" means in this space application. The astronaut was free to position his spacecraft in any attitude without actually changing its fixed orbital path.

Gemini astronauts have these same space control capabilities, but in additon are able to move from one orbit to another; this requires "guidance"—a method of determining precisely where the spacecraft is going and what has to be done to get it to its destination in space. To achieve this versatility, Gemini requires not only control on a given orbital track but guidance from one orbital track to another. Where Mercury had an ASCS (Attitude Stabilization and Control System), Gemini has ACME (Attitude Control and Maneuver Electronics) hooked up to its inertial guidance system.

ACME consists of primary and secondary rate gyro packages (each containing three gyros) to sense pitch, roll and yaw rates, a solid-state power inverter to change the current from DC to AC, and two small computers known as ACE (Attitude Control Electronics) and OAME (Orbit Attitude and Maneuver Electronics).

Basically, it is through these components that signals are generated to activate the various control or maneuver jets on Gemini.

The inertial platform reports how far and in what direction Gemini has travelled in relation to its starting point in space.

It stays perfectly horizontal and in a north-south alignment, regardless of gyrations of its host vehicle. Gemini is the first U.S. manned spacecraft to employ inertial guidance fully.

Most of a typical Gemini mission, however, is concerned with properly establishing the craft's attitude for a given segment of the mission. For this, it has nine distinct "modes" of operation available to the astronauts—six automatic, one combining automatic and manual, and two manual.

The various modes are selected by pushing buttons on the control panel. Only one mode can be operative at a time. The automatic attitude modes are called Horizontal, Orbit, Computer Radar, Retro and Re-entry. The combination mode is called Rate Command and manual modes are Direct Command and Single Pulse.

In general, signals are received during any of these modes by ACE for initial processing. Commands are then relayed to OAME (pronounced OH–ME) to fire the proper reaction jets.

Soon after separation from the Titan II booster, the Horizontal button will give control of the capsule to the horizon scanners. The capsule will be automatically oriented with the earth, and the inertial platform will be realigned to set a base reference from which any future maneuvers can be calculated.

The majority of flight time will likely be spent in Orbit mode, designed to hold the capsule steady, nose forward and tilted down about five degrees, with minimum expenditure of fuel and power.

The rate of deviation from the reference attitude of Orbit mode is limited to $\frac{5}{100}$ degree per second. (At this rate, it would take two hours to make one 360-degree roll.) Attitude information is taken from the horizon scanners and rate information is artificially created at a total system power requirement of less than three watts—about what it takes to light a Christmas tree light bulb. The power-consuming attitude and rate gyros are bypassed.

When the astronauts take command themselves, they will probably choose the Rate Command mode. With the control stick, they can pitch, roll or yaw the ship in any direction as quickly or slowly as they desire but when the stick returns to a neutral position, the rate gyros take over reducing and holding the rate of pitch, roll or yaw to less than ¼ degree per second. It is sort of an "instant stabilizer."

The Direct Command mode is just what the name implies; commands from the pilot go directly from the stick to the jets, bypassing ACE and OAME. Two sticks are provided, one for the 25-pound thrust control jets, the other for 100-pound thrust maneuver jets.

Single Pulse (for fuel conservation) is essentially the same as Direct Command, although ACE and OAME are required to time the jet-pulses electronically. Control jets fire one 20-millisecond (thousandth of a second) burst at a time while maneuver jets fire one 250-millisecond burst.

During Single Pulse, the pilot must move his stick 50 per cent of the way in a given direction to establish the direction he wants the jets to move him, then another ten per cent to fire a single burst. The stick must be moved again each time a burst is desired.

Computer and Radar modes are used during rendezvous maneuvers to determine when and how jets should be fired to match altitude and orbital period with the target vehicle. In effect, they "aim and fire" the Gemini spacecraft at its target.

The computer takes information from tracking ground stations and the inertial platform, tells the control system to maintain proper attitude and, through displays on the control panel, tells the astronauts when to fire maneuver jets.

When radar sighting is achieved, the radar unit is given control and supplies information to allow further closure. Finally, with visual contact and probably in the Rate Command mode, the astronauts will jockey the craft to a physical connection with the target.

Two automatic modes remain—Retro and Re-entry. Before the Retro button is pushed, the rear portion of the Gemini vehicle, called the Equipment Section, must be jettisoned to clear the retrograde rockets in an adjoining section for firing. Then, under Retro, the spacecraft is automatically turned 180 degrees to place the blunt end forward and tilted up 23 degrees from horizontal.

After retro-rockets are fired to slow the capsule for re-entry, the retrograde section of the ship (which contains OAME) is also jettisoned. The remaining portion, called the Re-Entry Body, is equipped with a heat shield like the Mercury spacecraft.

In the Re-entry mode, the spacecraft is maneuverable. Its center of gravity is offset so that it re-enters the atmosphere with a slight angle of attack which tends to produce a certain amount of lift. With this condition and by using attitude control jets mounted in the nose, Gemini can be rolled in a desired direction, permitting deviation of some 100 miles on either side of a simple ballistic re-entry path and several hundred miles up or down range.

Two landing methods for Gemini have been considered. The early Gemini flights will return just as the Mercury spacecraft finally touched down—a water landing by parachute. However, the second method of landing under consideration, one that will permit a landing on *terra firma* instead of at sea like the Mercury spacecraft, is a system built around an inflatable wing or paraglider.

A giant parachute can bring the Gemini spacecraft down to a soft water landing or a harder earth landing. In the latter case, Gemini astronauts have the ability to parachute from their spacecraft as it falls to earth beneath the giant chute. This will prevent any injury to the astronauts, for a parachute landing of any kind on the ground involves an element of danger and injury.

The paraglider concept would work this way: At approximately 60,000 feet, a drogue chute would be deployed; at 40,000 feet, the inflatable wing would be deployed, suspending the spacecraft in a generally horizontal position on five cables—one fixed at the nose, two fixed at the rear, and two attached to winches at the rear.

The two astronauts would, in effect, become glider pilots at this point. Movement of the control stick would provide a technique of steering which would be similar to a parachute jumper pulling static lines to make his chute slip one way or another.

Fig. 11-3. Early model of the "Rogallo Wing" to be used in later flight of Gemini to glide the spacecraft to an earth landing after re-entry has been achieved. (NASA)

In this manner, the spacecraft would glide as far as 35 miles from 40,000 feet, and land on skids at a predetermined landing area.

There's a valid reason for developing rendezvous techniques. An important factor involved in a flight to the moon or any planet concerns propulsion energy which alone can power a spacecraft to its destination. The heavier the spacecraft, the

Fig. 11-4. Artist's conception of the Gemini spacecraft making an earth landing with the steering mechanism employed in the paraglider inflated wing. The type of skids (wire brushes) slows the spacecraft quicker than regular wheels. (NASA)

more propulsion energy required. This is a fundamental physical law. As our space missions become more complex and ambitious, our spacecraft will become heavier. As the spacecraft become heavier, they will become larger, and the boosters standing on launch pads will tower to greater heights. Fuels can help a bit; they can give off additional energy or power—but not too much. It is then obvious that as spacecraft achieve very large sizes and weights, boosters may reach the point where they become inordinately large. This growth factor is paralleled by other forms of transportation vehicles, such as ships and aircraft. These have reached, or are reaching, the point where size has distinct limitations, and other stratagems are necessary to overcome the drawbacks of very large dimensions.

In astronautics, size limitations are even more painful. At our present stage of space development, for instance, the cost of developing a new set of vehicles for each new and larger space objective becomes tremendous. Space scientists have recognized this for many years; they have concluded in many cases that some form of space flight technique should be established which would not require extraordinarily huge boosters. The technique they have come up with is called by many names—orbital rendezvous, orbital interception or refueling in space. Whatever the name of the technique, it embodies some form of refueling of a spacecraft. Its aim is to set a limit on the building of larger and larger rocket vehicles, to permit some terminal size that has the capability of establishing contact in space and adding to the final spacecraft the extra propulsion energy and other supplies required for a deep-space journey.

The Gemini program is expected to master the rendezvous technique and provide the additional fuel for space maneuvers. Let's see how it works. If we take an imaginary trip to Cape Kennedy where Gemini is ready to be launched, we will observe the following scene:

Along the Cape Kennedy beach, a powerful Titan II booster rears high above the shoreline. Atop this giant two-stage rocket is the shape of the Gemini capsule, a giant television tube lying on its wide end, similar in design to the bell-shaped Mercury but 20 per cent larger in size. The spacecraft is clear and sharp against the blue sky, framed neatly in the sunlight. But on this morning the Titan II will not fly. The two astronauts assigned to this particular mission are busy on the ground, closer to the line of Atlas launch complexes. The star of the show on this particular morning is Atlas-Agena B, a husky booster and satellite payload that plays a special role in the Gemini program. Atlas-Agena B is

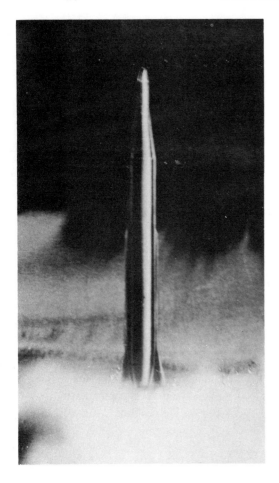

Fig. 11-5. Artist's conception of Atlas-Agena launch vehicle lifting off its pad. After burn out of the Atlas stage, it separates and the Agena stage is fired for the first time, placing it into an earth parking orbit. (NASA)

an old and familiar workhorse vehicle; it has launched Samos, Midas and other satellites and it has sent Ranger to the moon and Mariner to Venus and Mars.

The scene is familiar. The upper portion of the Atlas is covered with brilliant ice from the lox (liquid oxygen tanks), vapor plumes from the vent valves. Then, suddenly, the bluish-white vapors vanish. The valves are closed, the tanks sealed and pressurized as the countdown reaches zero. The small stabilizing vernier rockets spit flame, followed by the

volcanic gush of fire from the three main engines. Shackles
fly back, and the Atlas thunders under the sky. Many minutes
later, after Atlas has disappeared, Agena B is in orbit. For
the next 20 hours or more, every detail of that orbit is measured with painstaking care. Information from optical trackers,
radar scanners, and telemetry signals are fed into rows of
computers. The orbit, velocity, inclination, apogee, perigee is
measured down to the finest degree.

Hours later the Gemini project director has the information
he needs. His requirement is to fire the Titan II booster with
its two-man Gemini spacecraft so that it will be inserted into
its own orbit at the precise moment, not only in time but in
space as well. When the Gemini moves away from its own
booster rocket, in free fall, it must be within close proximity

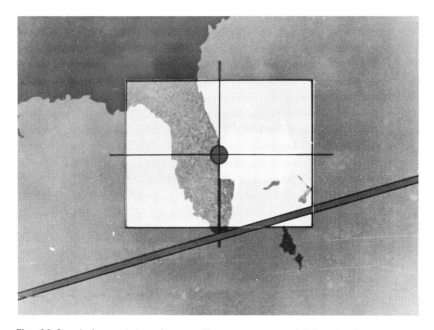

Fig. 11-6. A frame taken from a film sequence pertaining to the
proposed Gemini mission, illustrating the "window of launch" concept, a vital consideration affecting the success of rendezvous in
earth orbit. (NASA)

to the Agena B launched previously. It must be moving along the same plane so that the two spacecraft—one an unmanned satellite and the other manned—do not drift too far apart. Their angle of orbit in terms of perigee and apogee must be the same. Their velocities must be close.

Figure 11-6, taken from a film sequence pertaining to the proposed Gemini mission, illustrates the "window of launch" concept, a vital consideration affecting the success of rendezvous in earth orbit.

The "window of launch" concerns optimum time to launch the second vehicle so that its orbit is in the same plane as the orbit of the target vehicle, and with a phase relationship between the two vehicles, close enough to allow the craft to come together for the docking maneuver without excessive expenditure of fuel.

A vehicle launched at Cape Kennedy will assume an orbital plane that moves through the center of the earth, similar to the plane of the equator, but at a different angle. Although the plane of orbit of the vehicle remains constant in space, its relationship to Cape Kennedy constantly changes as the earth rotates.

The launching site moves out from under the path of the orbit and passes beneath it at just two points in a 24-hour rotation of the earth. It is only once every 24 hours, however, that Cape Kennedy's position in relation to the orbit is the same as it was at the time of launch. And it is in this period of time lasting just an instant that a second vehicle may be launched ideally into the same plane of orbit as its target vehicle.

This fleeting period of time is the "window of launch." If Cape Kennedy is allowed to move away from this optimum position before launching the second vehicle, the orbital angle of the second craft is different than that of the target. The further Cape Kennedy moves, the greater the angle differential of the orbital planes. The spacecraft can correct this difference in angle by changing its course in space, but to do so requires a considerable amount of fuel in relation to its fuel capacity.

The diagonal stripe in the photo represents the orbit of the target vehicle. The small arrow represents the short duration of the time segment (launch window). The longer arrow shows how the time in the window of launch can be extended by fuel provisions in the Gemini craft combined with proper launch techniques.

Finally, the information is in. The exact moment to launch Gemini is known. The Titan II stands ready. No fumes pour from lox tanks; there's no screaming of fuel pipes as liquid oxygen pours into the rocket from a line of tank trucks; no topping off—none of the lengthy preparations that went into the final Atlas countdown. The Titan II is an advanced booster fueled by a hypergolic fuel that is self-igniting and far more powerful than liquid oxygen. At launch time the booster stands ready and the astronauts are strapped down, waiting to be hurled into space. Around the other side of the world Agena B sweeps around the planet, rushing closer and closer. It plunges through space, then soars close to the Cape. The firing command rings out in the ground control blockhouse now called Gemini Control. Titan II comes alive with startling, explosive suddenness. From the curving flame bucket on the pad beneath the rocket engines, steam howls outward, tinged with a bright yellow color. The booster pushes away from the earth unlike the fiery Atlas. The flame from Titan II is almost transparent, more pink than red, and there is very little smoke with the characteristic burning of hypergolic fuel. But through binoculars, the shock-wave patterns in the flame are very clear.

This first stage is powerful—430,000 pounds thrust slam sound waves hard against the Cape. Despite the great weight of more than 150 tons, the rocket rushes upward with startling speed. Soon the glare is a pinpoint, then it winks out completely. Titan II bends more and more toward the horizontal, and then the first stage booster is exhausted. Valves snap closed, combustion dies with a shriek. Then, another explosion in the abrupt silence. The single rocket engine—100,000 pounds of thrust—gives life to the upper stage. The gravity forces that had fallen off begin once again to build up against the bodies of the two astronauts lying side by side in the spacecraft. The second stage booster accelerates with tremendous speed. Long seconds later, its flame creating an enormous billowing and filmy clouds of ionized gases, the desired speed is reached. The engine shuts down. Posigrade rockets fire to separate the spacecraft from the empty, useless

Fig. 11-7. Artist's concept of the Titan II booster lifting the two-man Gemini spacecraft into rendezvous orbit with the Agena target vehicle. (NASA)

Fig. 11-8. Artist's concept of the launch phase of a Titan II and two-man Gemini spacecraft. Here the first stage of Titan is separated after its 430,000 pounds of thrust has been expended.

second-stage booster and the Gemini vehicle edges ahead of the Titan II upper stage.

Gemini is in orbit. The Agena B is slightly higher than the manned spacecraft, 12 miles ahead. Immediately, the two astronauts receive confirmation of their own orbit from the tracking stations on earth. Computers whir at full speed to provide additional data in relation to both orbits. The order to rendezvous is flashed from ground control and inside the manned spacecraft radar equipment locks on to its target. The astronauts peer through angled windows that provide excellent visibility of the area of space through which Gemini is hurtling at nearly 18,000 miles an hour. A brilliant flashing beacon on the satellite assures the astronauts that it will remain visible when both space vehicles swing around the dark side of the earth.

The astronauts are ready to fire the Gemini's translational rockets for its rendezvous maneuver. But the orders from earth are different. Drift! Additional reports are flashed from the earth stations to the manned spacecraft. The computers indicate that for the Gemini to close in to Agena, the maneuvers would require an excessive consumption of fuel. Agena will close in to Gemini.

Agena, an engine with a heavy fuel supply, has restart capability in orbit. The ground stations flash commands to the robot brain of the satellite. Reaction jets position Agena exactly as desired. Then valves flip open and fuel explodes in the combustion chamber of the Agena rocket motor. The satellite decelerates slightly, edges just a bit down in its earth orbit. The differences are very small in terms of earth orbit, but they are extremely—critically—important in terms of the two vehicles in space and their relative positions.

Again the computers display their answers. Gemini and Agena are much closer now. The astronauts work as a superb team. They establish a new attitude for their spacecraft, and handling their controls with great sensitivity they finally fire their translational rockets. Brief bursts of power guide the Gemini smoothly into an adapter extending from the Agena, and the spacecraft and the satellite are joined. With the Agena

Fig. 11-9. Artist's conception of Gemini spacecraft using maneuvering rockets to close in on the Agena target vehicle. (NASA)

engine and its fuel supply, the astronauts have an additional maneuvering capability and another step to the moon has been taken.

Space navigation is still another step toward the moon. Once a spacecraft has achieved a true control and guidance capability, the next step is reaching its destination by navigating along the way. The system of finding the way in space will be somewhat complex. However, scientists have taken a page from marine navigational techniques. Gemini astronauts may determine where they are in orbit simply by opening the hatch and taking a "look." Sightings with a simple, handheld navigational device called a stadimeter would provide reliable range data without the use of digital computers. In fact, this unique concept would solve many of the problems

Fig. 11-10. Artist's conception of rendezvous achieved by the Gemini spacecraft and the Agena vehicle. (NASA)

of space navigation with a single lightweight, manual piece of equipment. The technique would be restricted to solution of orbital navigation problems, but would apply for any orbit—such as around the moon, or in planetary landings.

Why the interest in a manual device over an automatic system? System reliability is a major objective, and man is visualized as the basic computer and navigational device. This basic philosophy—that only man offers the reliability needed —has been practiced for years in aircraft and ship navigation. All equipment for this purpose is used to aid the navigator, fully utilizing man's reasoning powers. Engineers designing spacecraft are well aware that attempts to increase navigational reliability through "backup" systems increase weight— the spaceman's Waterloo. As a result, a new approach was needed, one precluding the use of power, on-board computers and automatic equipment of all kinds which are susceptible to component failure.

The new stadimetric device uses only manual and visual alignment and requires no electronics. Computations are few and simple, and the device can be operated from a limited field of view. It can be designed for use through the porthole of a space vehicle. Size and weight are small, equivalent to a small hand-held sextant.

The astronaut will use the stadimeter to determine optically the range of the space vehicle from the earth. Looking at the earth's curvature through the limited field-of-view device similar to a wide-angle, lower-power telescope, he will see three small arcs which he will adjust so that they cross at a single point. The readout will be an angle which is dependent upon the vehicle's range from the earth. This angle can easily be translated to range through the use of simple tables prepared before the flight.

Using a mechanical analog computer, the astronaut can determine the safety of the orbit, and the altitude and orbital location of the space vehicle at any future time. Measurements may be made while the hatch of the vehicle is either open or closed. For interior operation through a porthole, it would be necessary to maneuver the vehicle so that a portion of the earth's disc is visible. The device could be mounted or hand-held at the porthole.

Rendezvous, docking and navigating through space are only part of the Gemini mission. We still have much to learn about the reactions of men in space. What happens to blood circulation, to digestion, to respiration after a man has been weightless for a week or two? Can he operate more efficiently after

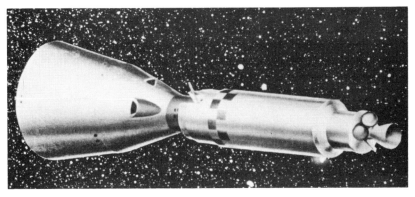

Fig. 11-11. Artist's conception of the Gemini spacecraft and the Agena vehicle joined and maneuvered as a single unit. (NASA)

being in space for a week or more? Can he carry out celestial-navigation assignments with accuracy? How will he maneuver his spaceship—efficiently, or with awkward movements? Gemini will answer these questions.

Can a man operate as a mechanic in space? On the earth, turning a wrench is an easy task. One simply fits the wrench around a nut—and pushes or pulls. But this is a complicated operation in space. The astronaut is weightless. When he turns a wrench in one direction, he is subject to Newton's Third Law of Motion that states every action has an opposite and equal reaction. As he turns the wrench, his body will move in the opposite direction.

Here on earth, a man plants his feet solidly against the floor. The weight of his body against the floor, the friction of his shoes, and other factors keep him in one place. He can exert his energy turning the wrench—and remain in position on his feet. We can understand this problem in another way. There is nothing to sitting down in a chair. But one cannot "just sit down" on a chair in space. On earth, when we bend our knees and relax our leg muscles, gravity pulls us down. But in space our body would not move toward the chair. Instead, our legs would come up and we would remain floating in the one spot where we tried to sit.

Therefore, it is the task of Gemini astronauts to carry out hundreds of experiments to see what tasks man can perform while he is weightless. The answers to these experiments will be put into good use by the Apollo astronauts to follow.

12

Project Apollo

$V^2 = 2GM/r.$

This is a basic formula that will help transport man to the moon and return. It's the formula that will carry man to the other planets in our solar system and to deeper exploration of space than we have heretofore dreamed.

$V^2 = 2GM/r$ is the formula for escape velocity—the speed at which spacecraft must travel after launching to escape the earth's gravitational pull. This speed amounts to seven miles per second, 420 miles per minute, or 25,200 miles per hour. As we have seen earlier, Mercury and Gemini space flights were in the neighborhood of 17,500 miles per hour—a free fall or orbital speed around the earth. It was enough speed to maintain orbital flight for a few orbits up to a few days and, in the case of Gemini, up to two weeks.

However, the flight to the moon in the Apollo spacecraft will require the 25,000 miles per hour escape velocity speed to hurl a three-man spaceship on its round trip to the moon. In order to accomplish this mission—the greatest of the space endeavors scheduled for this decade—control and guidance systems take on the greatest importance.

From here on earth the problem of rocketing to the moon appears a simple one. After all, the moon can be seen. Why not just launch a rocket straight to the moon? The astronauts can see where they left from and where they are going. This is true, but it's not that simple; there's more to the problem than meets the eye. In navigating a vehicle between two points on earth, one thing is basic: both of these points remain fixed with respect to each other. In travelling through space, however, the origin of the spaceship and its destination are moving rapidly with respect to each other. Any errors will lead to disaster.

The mathematical problem of describing the trajectory of transfer between origin and destination in outer space is based on a number of new factors that the spaceship's "astrogator" must consider. He has to make his spaceship's position, velocity and time in flight coincide exactly with similar factors concerning his destination. If the "astrogator" matches position and time but not velocity, his spaceship may become a flaming meteor or he may find his grave at the core of a new surface crater, depending upon whether his destination is a planet or an airless moon. If he matches the planet's velocity, acceleration and position, but at the wrong time, the destination is not there when his spaceship arrives. If he hasn't enough rocket fuel aboard to chase and catch up with his destination, he may find that he'll fall into an orbit in which his destination might chase the spacecraft forever.

To put it another way, the Apollo spaceship's course to the moon will not be set by aiming at the place where the moon is at the time of launch, but where it will be some 70 hours after launch. With the earth moving 6,800 miles an hour relative to the sun, and the moon travelling 2,300 miles per hour relative to the earth, accuracy and timing are critical. As a result, guidance and control techniques are also critical, as we shall see.

The original plan to rocket Americans to the moon envisioned a gigantic booster that would be launched from earth into orbit; from its orbit, it would be rocketed to the moon for a landing with three astronauts as passengers. A mammoth booster called Nova had been designed for this moon flight. Described as a "volcano packaged neatly into the biggest tin can ever," the Nova booster would have a first-stage thrust at lift-off of 12,000,000 pounds. Nova was designed with a 45-foot diameter first and second stage; it would have towered nearly 400 feet high in its vertical launch position with a gross launch of 10,000,000 pounds. Its conception, however, was turned down by NASA space scientists who believe that a journey to the moon could be accomplished with a smaller booster called Saturn.

This booster, called the Saturn C-5, in its first stage

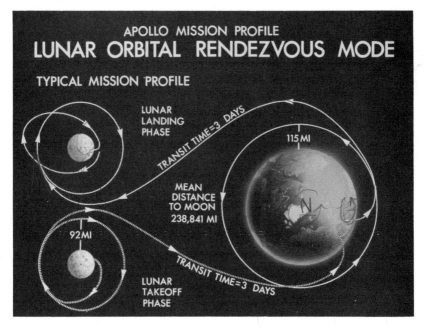

Fig. 12-1. Apollo mission plan. (NASA)

has five F-1 engines each delivering 1,500,000 pounds of thrust, for a total of 7,500,000 pounds at launch. Each F-1 engine stands 20 feet high and measures 14 feet across the nozzle exit. The C-5's fuel tanks are 33 feet in diameter and the first stage alone stands 140 feet high. Even Stage II is enormous. It also is 33 feet in diameter but half the height of the first stage. It burns high energy fuels through five J-2 engines, each of which delivers 200,000 pounds thrust for a second-stage power rating of 1,000,000 pounds. This giant booster with only these two stages can—in a single firing— place into low earth orbit a payload of more than 100 tons.

Topping the two stages of the Saturn launch vehicle is the Apollo payload—18 feet in diameter and 60 feet in length, powered by a single J-2 engine. All told, the three-stage Saturn C-5, with its Apollo payload (Command Service Modules, escape tower and escape rocket) will stand 364 feet

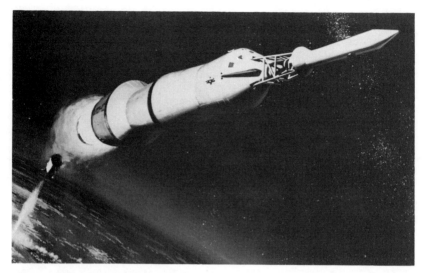

Fig. 12-2. Artist's drawing of Saturn V roaring skyward burning
15 tons of fuel per second for two and one half minutes to achieve
its acceleration. (NASA)

high at launch time—65 feet taller than the Statue of Liberty.
It will weigh more than 3,000 tons when its mighty engines
begin to blast off from earth.

The flight plan for the moon landing calls for launching
into an earth orbit about 100 miles high. The ground-based
mission control center will calculate the trajectory required
to rendezvous with the moon, and the exact time that the
second stage engines must be fired to push the spaceship to
escape velocity and on a collision course. While orbiting the
earth in the weightless state, the astronauts will be able to get
up and move around their spaceship inside the 12-foot tall
Command module which will have a "backroom" service
module carrying the power generator, pressure system, propellant and engine for mid-course correction and the fuel cell.
The third compartment will be the Lunar Excursion Module
(LEM) that will detach from the mother ship in orbit around
the moon and drop two of the crew down to the lunar surface,
while the third astronaut remains with the orbiting Apollo

spaceship. This plan does away with the task of depositing the entire spaceship on the moon and having to lift it off again. The more powerful Nova would have made this possible, but scientists felt that it was impractical.

After landing on the moon, the two astronauts will collect rocks and samples and take scientific measurements to bring back to earth. When it's time to rendezvous with the orbiting Apollo spaceship, the astronauts will reenter the LEM. They'll launch it with a 3,000-pound thrust engine and guide it into a curving course designed to intercept the orbiting Apollo command module. When the two spaceships rendezvous and dock, and the astronauts transfer back to the Apollo spaceship, the LEM will be dropped off. Apollo will then be rocketed back to earth with the blast from its 200,000-pound thrust J-2 engine—enough kick to put it in a rendezvous trajectory with earth.

The landing on the moon by American astronauts, however, will not take place until a number of other missions have first been accomplished. The NASA space program is predicated on the assumption that crawling comes before walking, and a lot of crawling is still required. This means that the first flights of Apollo to the moon will be strictly "sightseeing trips." Even before this "circumlunar" trip, orbital flights in the Apollo spacecraft will be made, and for practice, a number of rendezvous tests with the LEM will take place.

The sightseeing trip to the moon will follow the escape velocity flight pattern for leaving the earth's gravitational pull—orbit followed by launching into deep space from the orbital path. The idea of this survey flight is to bring the Apollo close by the moon's surface, around the far side of the moon in a giant swing, and then back toward earth. In the circumlunar flight the crew will, for the first time in flight, perform the complicated guidance and navigation task of steering the spaceship to the moon. They will steer in an orbit around the moon, and on its flight back toward the earth. While in the vicinity of the moon, the crew will be able personally to survey the landing site that it will later use in the manned lunar mission.

Fig. 12-3. Artist's concept of the second stage (S-II) engines burning out after six and one half minutes and separating. The S-IV B third stage then ignites a single J-2 engine of 200,000 pounds total thrust. The third stage will burn for two and three quarters minutes, placing the configuration in earth orbit. (NASA)

Fig. 12-4. Artist's drawing of the Apollo configuration still attached to the third stage on its trajectory path toward the moon at a speed of 25,000 mph. The second burning of the third-stage engine for five minutes is necessary to overcome the earth's gravitational attraction. (NASA)

Fig. 12-5. Artist's concept of the S-IV B stage after circling the earth one and one half times. When all phases check out, this stage will ignite for the second time at a precisely determined moment to place it on a lunar trajectory. (NASA)

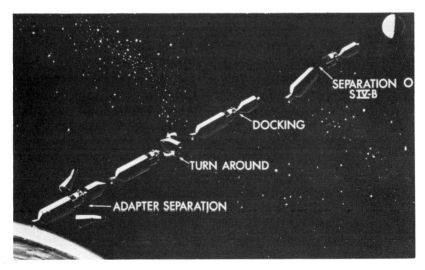

Fig. 12-6.   Sequence of docking and third-stage separation maneuver. (NASA)

Fig. 12-7.   Artist's conception of the command and service modules separating from the third stage. The service module propulsion system is used to turn the configuration around for docking nose-to-nose with the Lunar Excursion Module. (NASA)

Fig. 12-8.   Docking maneuver of the Apollo command module with the Lunar Excursion Module. (NASA)

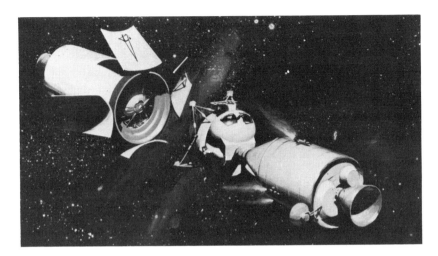

Fig. 12-9. After the docking of LEM (Lunar Excursion Module) and the Apollo module, the housing around the LEM falls away and the S-IV B Saturn third stage separates, using the service module propulsion system. (NASA)

Fig. 12-10. LEM's arrival in the vicinity of the moon. Orientation controls will be used to turn and ignite the service module and place it in orbit about 100 miles above the moon's surface. (NASA)

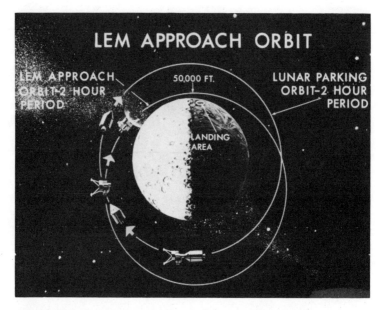

Fig. 12-11.   Schematic of LEM's approach orbit. (NASA)

Fig. 12-12.   LEM's lunar orbit. (NASA)

Fig. 12-13. The engine of the Lunar Excursion Module landing stage is ignited to provide 8,800 pounds of thrust for about one minute. This impulse will place the LEM in an approach orbit that has the same time period of revolution as that of the command module. (NASA)

Fig. 12-14. The landing engine (8,800-pound thrust) achieving lunar descent. The engine can be throttled down to 1,100 pounds of thrust to place LEM in hovering position, 300 feet above the lunar surface. After selection of landing points, the LEM will descend slowly to the lunar surface at speeds less than seven miles. (NASA)

But if the mission to the moon must be precise, then the return journey to the earth must be even more precise. For the three men in Apollo must return in a trajectory calculated to the ultimate. Apollo must enter the upper edges of the earth's atmosphere within narrow limits in order to come down in a landing corridor no more than 40 miles wide. Forty miles may seem to be a rather large width for the flight of a vehicle, but not when the spacecraft is moving so fast that it can cross the 40-mile corridor in less than six seconds. Moreover, the starting point for the entry corridor begins nearly 250,000 miles away; the mid-course corrections made along the return flight must be calculated with the utmost care, and then must be made with virtually *no* margin of error. The accuracy required for this maneuver is akin to hitting dead-center, across an entire football field, a target no larger than a nickel.

Let's take a closer look at the mission to the moon. The Apollo spaceship will approach the moon along an orbit that carries the spaceship close to the lunar surface and then around the far side. The retro rockets will slow down the heavy spaceship so that it falls into an orbit around the moon. If the Apollo spacecraft were to approach the surface directly —such as in an impact landing—the danger of failure would be increased. Suppose, during this maneuver, the propulsion system failed to operate. The result would be fatal; the spaceship would continue on its collision course directly into the lunar surface. On the other hand, if there's a failure in the orbiting maneuver, the spaceship can be directed back to earth.

Normally, after it has decelerated and been "captured" by the moon's gravity, the Apollo will discharge its LEM with two astronauts—a maneuver similar to the Gemini spacecraft pulling away from its docking position with the Agena B. As it approaches the lunar surface at an angle, LEM will decelerate with its rockets. Over the landing site, it will then descend vertically. As it reaches the lunar surface, its speed must be just about zero—almost like that of a helicopter touching down gently on the earth. On this airless neighbor of earth, everything in the landing maneuver is an infinitely fine, constantly adjusted manipulation of rocket energy. A special landing gear on LEM absorbs the shock of any terrain.

Once on the moon, the two-man crew will immediately check out all systems. From their landing site they will be able to see the earth from their line-of-sight area; this will permit direct communications with home planet continuously. Because of the distance, a time lag of just under two seconds will change real-time computer measurements by this fraction of time. Once LEM is checked out, the astronauts will then begin a few days of exploration and experiments.

They will leave the LEM through an airlock and climb down a long ladder. But even in the pressure suits that must be worn, their task will be eased, because on this airless, soundless, weatherless world, the surface gravity is only one-sixth that of earth, and even the heaviest spacesuit will be no burden to its wearer.

Fig. 12-15. After the two astronauts have climbed from the LEM to the Command Module, the LEM will be detached and left in lunar orbit. (NASA)

Although the moon explorers will not travel too far from LEM, future surveys of the moon by men will require some of man's early lore—taking bearings on landmarks and on the stars. But the most critical part of the visit to the moon is the launching for a one-stop trip back to earth. The countdown will be precise. The two-man crew must launch into virtually the same orbit that the Apollo Command Module is travelling overhead. Part of the LEM will act as the launch pad and will be left behind, while the module containing the two astronauts surges into space to rendezvous and dock with the Apollo Command Module. They will transfer to Apollo; LEM will be thrust away, and Apollo will be made ready for the 250,000-mile trip back to earth.

Earth will be seen easily by the three men in the spaceship. But the return trip will reverse the procedure that sent Apollo to the moon. Instead of aiming for the earth, the Apollo will be programmed to rendezvous where the earth will be in 66 hours. Of course, computers on earth will plan the proper

Fig. 12-16.   Returning to earth in Command Module. (NASA)

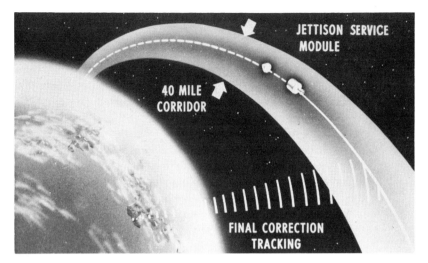

Fig. 12-17.   Scheme for reentry of the Command Module. (NASA)

trajectory for the "fall" back to terra firma. The Apollo engine
will burst into flame hurtling the spaceship in a faster orbit
until the 5,600-mile-an-hour escape velocity speed is acquired. At this point the power can be cut, for the escape velocity of the moon is much less than that of earth. When the
power is shut down and Apollo is moving along its desired
trajectory, return to the earth is guaranteed.

esc. from
moon

On the way, mid-course correction, changing slightly to the
exact direction, will be accomplished, so that the Apollo
will come down into the re-entry corridor at the precise moment and place as planned. How precise can best be ex-
plained by describing the earth as a merry-go-round on a
slowly moving truck with a bystander trying to jump on the
revolving platform—onto a particular spot on the turning platform. That's how precisely the guidance system must operate.

Good
Analogy

The landing on earth will be a fiery, blazing return. We
have seen how the Mercury and Gemini heat shields and
spacecraft heated up to a glowing orange after being slowed
by retrorockets for reentry to earth. However, Apollo will be
hurtling along at 25,000 miles per hour—seven miles per

second—when it slices into the upper reaches of earth's atmosphere and plunges into the barrier reefs of friction. Apollo will look like a great, flaming meteor crashing downward from space. Retrofire will slow it enough to slacken speed. Temperatures will halt their rise and begin to decrease rapidly. At the proper time, parachutes will open and lower Apollo gently to a landing—thereby completing for man the first deep space probe for a landing on another planet, and return.

To understand some of the problems of a flight to the moon, we must first take a long view of celestial mechanics—the application of mathematical methods to the study of motions of heavenly bodies. What this means is computing the ephemeris or table of predicted positions as a function of time of planets, comets or satellites. As we can readily see, practical problems in celestial mechanics usually lead to very complex solutions requiring batteries of high speed computers to analyze the mathematical equations and come up with the figures that scientists can use in their calculations. In order to understand more easily the problems of manned interplanetary flight, of which Apollo is the first, let's take a look at our solar system in relation to the earth and moon.

The solar system consists of one star, nine planets, 31 known moons, and thousands of smaller bodies. The star, which we

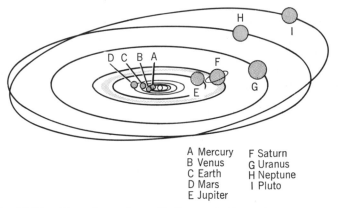

A Mercury	F Saturn
B Venus	G Uranus
C Earth	H Neptune
D Mars	I Pluto
E Jupiter	

Fig. 12-18.   The solar system with the sun in the center.

TABLE OF SOLAR SYSTEM

	Sun	Moon	Mercury	Venus	Earth	Mars	Jupiter	Saturn	Uranus	Neptune	Pluto
Diameter (miles)	870,000	2,170	3,100	7,750	7,970	4,140	87,300	71,000	32,000	31,000	3,700
Mean Distance From Sun (millions of miles)	—	—	36	67	93	142	484	887	1,785	2,800	3,675
Escape Velocity (miles per second)	387	1.5	2.6	6.4	7	4	37	22	13	14	?
Surface Gravity (Earth =1)	28	.16	.36	.86	1	.40	2.64	1.17	.91	1.12	?
Eccentricity of Orbit (circle =0)	—	.054	.206	.007	.017	.093	.048	.056	.047	.009	.248
Inclination to Ecliptic (degrees)	—	5.8	7	3.2	—	1.5	1.18	2.3	.46	1.46	17.8
Number of Satellites	—	—	0	0	1	2	12	9	5	2	0
Period of Revolution	—	27.3 days	88 days	224 days	365 days	1.9 years	11.9 years	29.4 years	84 years	164.8 years	247.7 years

call the sun, is at the center of the system, the nine planets arrayed around it in near-circles.

All planets move in the same direction around the sun. Orbital speeds are greatest near the sun, and decrease with distance from the sun. The closest planet, Mercury, makes one circuit in 88 days, and the farthest planet, Pluto, one in 248 years.

All planets lie very nearly in the same plane, Pluto being the notable exception, with its orbit tilted 17 degrees to the ecliptic (plane of the earth's orbit). The solar system is therefore shaped something like a pancake.

Bodies moving in circles around a central point do not lend themselves to travel from place to place, for the same reason that it is difficult to walk a straight line on a merry-go-round. Yet some factors about the solar system seem to invite interplanetary travel.

First, the space between the earth and other bodies in the solar system is a near-perfect vacuum. Only in such an environment can we move at speeds which make it practicable to travel interplanetary distances.

Second, the earth is one of the smaller planets, which means it has a comparatively small escape velocity and a comparatively thin atmosphere, hence less resistance to rapidly ascending and descending objects.

Third, the uniform direction of the planets makes it possible for an interplanetary traveller to use the orbital speed of one planet in launching himself to another. The fact that the planets are arranged in nearly the same plane makes uniformity of direction even more significant, as a vehicle that must be slanted away from the orbital plane of a departure planet does not derive full benefit from the planet's velocity.

Fourth, although the orbits of the planets are technically ellipses, their eccentricities or deviations from true circles are so slight that they can be termed near-circular. This means that energy requirements for transferring from one orbit to another are nearly the same for all points of departure along an orbit.

Fifth, most planets rotate in the same direction in which

they revolve about the sun. This means that a space vehicle launched from the surface of these planets can get a small but significant push by taking off in the direction of rotation.

There are two basic methods of starting a lunar or interplanetary flight from the earth: launch from the surface or from an established orbit around the earth. Both employ the curved flight path. Earlier, we discussed the popular misconception about space flight, in which vehicles leave the earth vertically and follow a more or less direct line of flight to other bodies. This is something like trying to drive straight up a mountainside, instead of following a long curved highway to the top.

Curved departure from earth is the natural method because it takes less energy to gain altitude on a more horizontal route than a vertical one, and because vertical ascent tends to cancel out the free ride supplied by rotational velocity.

There is little difference in technique between a surface launch and an orbital launch, aside from the fact that the former begins within the atmosphere, the latter in space. The chief distinction is in power requirements. A vehicle starting an interplanetary journey from a satellite orbit needs much less power than one starting from the surface, because it

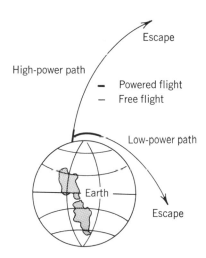

Fig. 12-19.   Escape paths.

already has 70 per cent of the velocity required for escape.

To reach another planet, a surface-launched vehicle accelerates along a curve until it has gained the required velocity. A vehicle orbiting the earth accelerates forward, breaks the satellite ellipse or circle, as the case may be, and curves outward. If acceleration is sufficient to increase circular velocity by a factor of 1.4, the vehicle achieves escape or parabolic velocity. To reach another planet, a velocity somewhat larger than that required for mere escape is needed. This is referred to as hyperbolic velocity.

In calculating a flight path to the moon, the astronautical engineer must consider—exclusive of vehicle performance—the gravitational fields of the earth, moon and sun, the earth's atmosphere, the earth's rotation on its axis, the moon's orbit around the earth, the inclination of the earth's axis to the ecliptic, the plane of the earth's orbit, and the inclination of the moon's orbit to the ecliptic.

The moon is not an easy target. Its diameter is about one fourth that of the earth. It travels in its orbit at a mean velocity at 2,268 miles per hour, and its distance from the earth alternates between 221,463 miles at perigee and 252,710 miles at apogee.

Due to the nearness of the moon, <u>it is not necessary to</u>

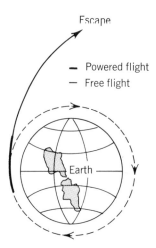

Fig. 12-20.   Departure from orbit.

accelerate to escape velocity for the flight, only to 99 per cent of it. A moon journey conducted in this fashion follows an elliptical curve relative to the earth, even though it is short of parabolic velocity by only a few miles per hour.

A rocket fired at the moon need not retain its peak velocity throughout the voyage. For about nine-tenths of the distance the earth's gravity restrains the vehicle's forward progress, gradually reducing speed built up during powered flight. At about 24,000 miles from the moon, however, the moon's gravity takes over. From this point the rocket picks up speed, as it is then "falling" toward the moon.

A short view of celestial mechanics can be taken from inside the spaceship as it departs for the moon. The astronauts will depend on a super sextant, on gyroscopes able to remain upright through violent tumbling and on pinhead-sized electronic parts. It will be totally contained on board the spaceship and will be capable of operation, if necessary, without information or instructions from earth. However, it has a built-in capability of accepting ground information and commands.

The Guidance and Navigation System that three U.S. astronauts will use to steer their Project Apollo spacecraft to the moon and back will be totally contained on board the spacecraft and will be capable of operation, if necessary, without information or instructions from earth. The system will also be capable of accepting ground information and commands.

The astronauts will have great flexibility in the way this Guidance and Navigation System (G&N) is operated, ranging from manual modes to automatic modes. This flexibility in what engineers call the man-machine interface represents one of the important advances being incorporated into the guidance and navigation design.

The job of getting the Project Apollo Spacecraft to the moon and back can be described in terms of the two principal functions of the G&N system.

The first function is navigation. This is determination of position in space and is similar to pinpointing position on earth as is done by a ship navigator at sea. In space, however, the job is considerably more complicated, and in order to de-termine an adequate orbit, one must know the past, present and predict the future position of the spacecraft.

The second function is guidance. Having established the position and velocity of the spacecraft, the system must then establish the steering direction and the necessary starting and stopping of the controllable engines in order to follow the road map established by the navigation function previously performed.

To carry out these functions, the Apollo G&N system will be composed of three principle subunits—an inertial measure-ment unit, an optical measurement unit and a computer unit —plus the displays and controls that relate the three and provide the flexible man-machine interface.

The inertial measurement unit (IMU) is an assembly of gyroscopes and accelerometers that can establish a fixed refer-ence, from within which it can measure the direction and speed of the spacecraft and determine any changes in either direction or speed.

The gyroscopes and accelerometers are mounted on a struc-ture at the center of the IMU called the inner member. The inner member, in turn, is mounted inside three spherical gim-bals, one for each principal axis of motion. The gyroscopes provide signals which are used to drive the gimbals to isolate the inner member from changes of spacecraft attitude and thus hold the inner member fixed. Accelerometers measure forces acting on the vehicle and, hence, keep track of its route within the gyroscopically-stabilized reference frame.

The optical measurement unit contains a telescope and a space sextant, plus associated displays and controls. The sextant is similar to nautical sextants except that it is used in an entirely new application—space—and embodies numer-ous automatic features.

The inertial measurement unit and the optical unit will be used by the crew to take navigational readings and to pinpoint spacecraft position in space on the route to the moon and back.

The third and one of the most important elements of the

system is a compact but extremely versatile digital computer which will translate the data gathered, both automatically and by the astronauts, into commands which will keep the vehicle on its course.

The G&N system will occupy an area about four feet high, two feet deep and three feet wide. It will mount on a wall of the spacecraft.

When astronauts are reclining in their couches and facing up toward the apex of the conical spacecraft for thrust phases of flight (boost, course corrections), the G&N system will be at the feet of the center crew member.

The center astronaut will be "astrogator." His couch will fold away during coasting periods so he can work with the G&N station.

During coast periods (earth and moon orbit, free fall along earth-moon and moon-earth trajectories), the navigator will

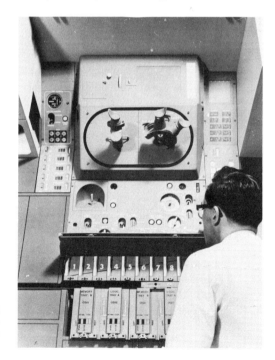

Fig. 12-21. Mockup of the guidance and navigation system to be used aboard the Apollo spacecraft. (M.I.T.)

make numerous angle sightings between stars and earth land-marks or moon landmarks. He will have controls to maneuver spacecraft attitude so as to point his optical instruments in desired directions.

Through the inertial measurement unit and optics controls and through a 16-button coded keyboard to the computer, the navigator will be able to operate the G&N system in several different configurations, depending on need and on flight phase.

For example, under navigator command, the computer will use optical sighting information to compute mooncraft posi-tion and velocity with respect to actual celestial moon or earth reference frames.

The inertial measurement unit will be used to guide the vehicle during re-entry and during powered flight phases when the rocket engines are fired, and will measure the corresponding position and velocity changes.

In still another configuration, the astronaut-navigator will be able to use star sighting to align his IMU reference frame to the orientation ideally suited for anticipated thrust ma-neuvers.

During earth orbit and moon orbit, the G&N, using data based on the astronaut's optical tracking information and IMU readings, will compute the precise orbit being followed and the precise time and place for a burst from the spacecraft rocket to place the vehicle on a trajectory to the moon or on a trajectory back to earth.

Under navigator command, the G&N also will initiate the split-second rocket firing, control and craft as it assumes a new trajectory, and cut off the rocket when appropriate.

The Apollo vehicle will not follow a single coasting tra-jectory to the moon and a single trajectory back to earth. Oc-casional course corrections, to achieve a new trajectory based on position and velocity needed to be gained for a moon or or earth intercept, will be made with the rocket engine. G&N will keep track of vehicle position and velocity at all times, compare this to moon or earth position, and calculate if cor-rections will be needed. Under navigator command, the G&N also will initiate these corrections.

During reentry into earth atmosphere, G&N will provide for control of spacecraft roll attitude through the vehicle's stabilization rockets, to bring the ship and its crew safely to its preselected landing site.

Data and commands exchanged between G&N subunits and between the G&N and the navigator will be radio-monitored by earth stations. The astronaut-navigator will be able to select manual as well as automatic overrides in virtually all G&N operations.

13

Unmanned Satellites

Before man can travel to other planets—even to our closest neighbor, the moon—he must first solve the mysteries of space which have defied centuries of observation. The space age dates back to October 4, 1957, when the Soviet Union launched the first Sputnik satellite into a simple orbit around the earth. The first United States satellite followed on January 31, 1958, when Explorer I was launched into orbit with 18 pounds of instruments designed to study micrometeorites, cosmic rays and temperature measurements. However, Explorer I turned in one unexpected result—notably the discovery of the Van Allen Radiation Belt. For a while scientists were unable to determine whether or not man could safely pierce this radiation field for orbital and deep space flights.

Since October 1957 man has hurled hundreds of satellites and probes into space in an effort to measure and examine this new element that will soon become his habitat as he speeds between the planets or orbits in huge laboratories. At least the Space Age is now out of its infancy. It will not be able to claim maturity, however, until the launching of men to the moon causes no more of a news flurry than does the launching of a weather or observation satellite today.

The perfection of manned space flight is still our primary goal. On the other hand, the particular part of the space program that has reached its goal and is rapidly becoming "commonplace" is that phase concerned with unmanned scientific satellites. Until the development of the larger, more powerful boosters, the United States space exploration program was limited to a series of smaller satellites like the Explorer, Pioneer and the Vanguard series. The development of the Atlas ICBM permitted us to launch the heavier satellites, including the manned Mercury spacecraft. The larger Titan II has made Gemini possible. Saturn will make Apollo possible. In one sense the unmanned scientific and meteorological satellite program has benefited by this weight-lifting limitation of the boosters. This has imposed on the space program an approach in which relatively single-purpose, specialized satellites have been launched into orbits uniquely suited to the particular set of experiments which they carry. The bits and pieces of these experiments are being fitted together like a giant jig-saw puzzle, from which a pattern has emerged for a better understanding of the space environment and even of our earth.

For example, Vanguard I led to the deduction of the "pearshaped" earth. This information has been of help to geologists who are trying to understand the characteristics of the earth's surface and its interior. From the data sent back by the Vanguard satellite family, geologists have been able to deduce the bending strength of the earth's crust and its resistance to known distorting forces. One interesting inference has also been drawn by the geologist—that this shape was set some 50 million years ago when the day was 23 hours and 30 minutes in length.

Echo is another satellite that has proved out in several ways. Originally launched as a passive communications satellite from which radio signals could be bounced and picked up by a receiver located elsewhere on earth, Echo has had additional uses. In size, it is the biggest satellite launched by man. Constructed as an inflatable sphere, 100 feet in diameter and made of mylar polyester plastic about half the thickness of the cellophane on a package of cigarettes, Echo carries no instruments to gather information and transmit it back to earth. On its surface, however, are two wafer-thin "beacon" transmitters powered by solar cells, which aid ground observers to locate the satellite. Since the transmitters are sunpowered, the signals fade when Echo passes around the dark side of the earth. Aside from communications uses, its most important contribution to scientists came after a series of solar flares erupting from the sun slightly changed Echo's orbit. From this information, upper atmosphere physicists were able to deduce that flares of this nature heated up the atmosphere, causing it to expand and increase in density at the altitudes of the Echo orbit.

This orbital data was later more thoroughly measured out and proved by later sophisticated Explorer satellites. Pioneer V was launched into an orbit around the sun and it continued transmitting until it was about 22.5 million miles out from earth. Another of the later scientific satellites is the Orbiting Solar Observatory or OSO, the first true observatory in orbit. It was designed to point selected experiments at the center of

Fig. 13-1.   Tiros weather satellite. (NASA)

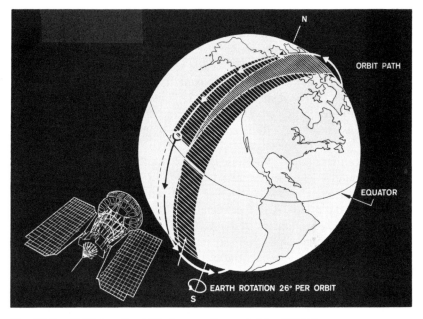

N

ORBIT PATH

EQUATOR

EARTH ROTATION 26° PER ORBIT

S

Fig. 13-2.   Orbital path of Nimbus weather satellite. (NASA)

the sun with the direction accurately measured by gas jets working in conjunction with electric servo-motors linked to the basic gyroscope. Utilizing the sun's power, this spacecraft must re-acquire and stabilize on the sun once each orbit, as it has done thousands of times with great precision. Thanks to the OSO, the so-called solar winds, or plasma which erupts from the sun, have aided scientists in planning designs of "space gliders" that would "fly" like a glider travelling on the wind currents.

The Tiros and Nimbus weather satellites, shooting photos of the weather on earth, have improved meteorology a hundredfold. No longer do hurricanes spawned in the Carribean or typhoons born in the Pacific Ocean waters off southeast Asia pose a threat. The weather satellites transmit photos of the birth of these storms and track them relentlessly so that warnings can be posted on time.

American industry's first venture into space occurred in 1962 when Telstar was launched by American Telephone and Telegraph Company with an assist by a NASA launch crew and booster. This was the first of a series of active communications satellites which hooked up Europe and the United States with a television link. The Relay communications satellites followed along with the ultimate in a global communications satellite hook-up—the Syncom.

Of all of the hundreds of satellites launched by man, Syncom was one of the most dramatic and impressive. The earlier communication satellites orbited in the familiar low encirclement of the earth. But the drum-shaped Syncom hovers 22,300 miles over the equator. This new breed of satellite appears motionless in the sky in a synchronous orbit. It moves at 6,800 miles per hour, a speed just fast enough for it to keep pace with a point on the somewhat more slowly rotating earth

Fig. 13-3. The actual flight model of Syncom III communications satellite. (Hughes Aircraft Company)

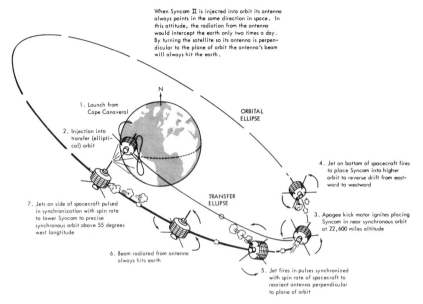

When Syncom II is injected into orbit its antenna always points in the same direction in space. In this attitude, the radiation from the antenna would intercept the earth only two times a day. By turning the satellite so its antenna is perpendicular to the plane of orbit the antenna's beam will always hit the earth.

N

1. Launch from Cape Canaveral

ORBITAL ELLIPSE

2. Injection into transfer (elliptical) orbit

4. Jet on bottom of spacecraft fires to place Syncom into higher orbit to reverse drift from eastward to westward

7. Jets on side of spacecraft pulsed in synchronization with spin rate to lower Syncom to precise synchronous orbit above 55 degrees west longtitude

TRANSFER ELLIPSE

3. Apogee kick motor ignites placing Syncom in near synchronous orbit at 22,600 miles altitude

6. Beam radiated from antenna always hits earth

5. Jet fires in pulses synchronized with spin rate of spacecraft to reorient antenna perpendicular to plane of orbit

Fig. 13-4.   Schematic of Syncom II communications satellite maneuvers since its launch July 26, 1963.   (NASA)

below, just as an Olympic runner racing on the outside must move faster to keep abreast of the runner in the inside lane.

Achieving a synchronous orbit is extremely difficult. After Syncom's first two stages are fired in the launch phase, the vehicle coasts southeast. During the lull, small attitude control jets turn its nose northward. Then the small third stage rocket is fired, reducing the angle of Syncoms orbit from 28 degrees to 17 degrees off the equatorial plane. Small bursts of jet power, fired on signal from the ground control station at Cape Kennedy, reduce the angle relative to the equator to near zero, and changes the elliptical shape of the orbit into a circle. Thus the satellite is made to appear virtually motionless. This synchronous satellite has always been theoretically the most practical method of linking world communications together. A mere three satellites anchored appropriately could blanket the whole world so that any point on earth will be in constant

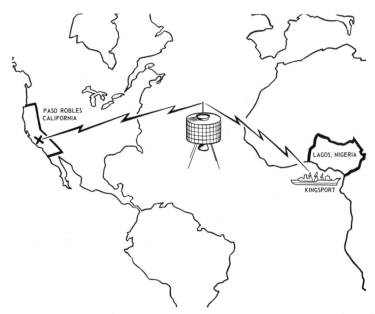

Fig. 13-5. In the longest direct line-of-sight telephone call ever made, Hughes Aircraft Company officials talked between California and Africa via Syncom 2 hovering in orbit 22,300 miles above the mid-Atlantic between two continents. (Hughes Aircraft Company)

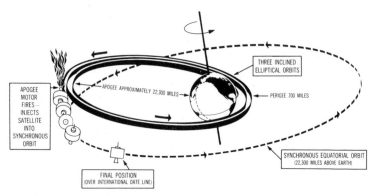

Fig. 13-6. Launch sequence of Syncom III, the "Olympic satellite." (Hughes Aircraft Company)

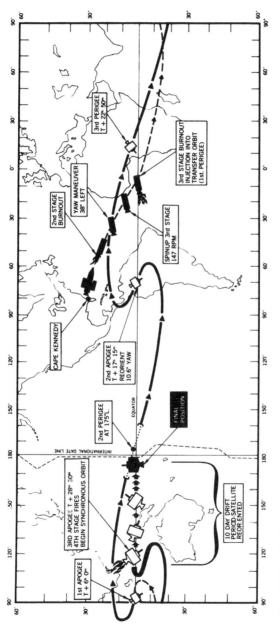

Fig. 13-7.   Orbiting sequence of Syncom C. (NASA)

line of sight with Syncom, whereas dozens of Telstar and Relay satellites would be required to perform the same mission as the three hovering satellites.

The second dramatic flight of an unmanned spacecraft is that of the Ranger VII, which flew to the moon for a crash landing while transmitting valuable photos of the lunar surface back to earth before impact and destruction. Although an earlier Soviet Lunik flight around the back side of the moon provided photos of the unseen face of earth's nearest neighbor, the Ranger VII spacecraft transported itself exactly as the scientists planned.

Halfway through its journey, Ranger VII changed course, slightly—at what's known as the mid-course correction point—

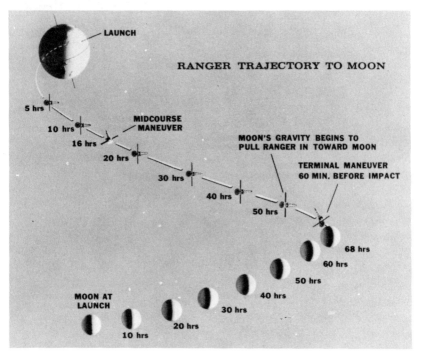

Fig. 13-8.   Ranger spacecraft course for lunar surface photography mission. (NASA)

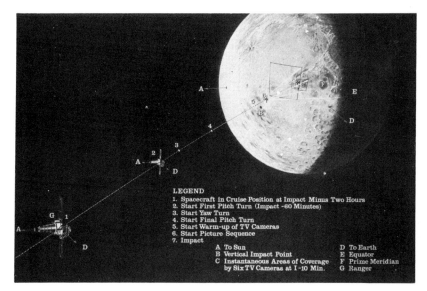

LEGEND
1. Spacecraft in Cruise Position at Impact Minus Two Hours
2. Start First Pitch Turn (Impact -60 Minutes)
3. Start Yaw Turn
4. Start Final Pitch Turn
5. Start Warm-up of TV Cameras
6. Start Picture Sequence
7. Impact

A To Sun   D To Earth
B Vertical Impact Point   E Equator
C Instantaneous Areas of Coverage F Prime Meridian
   by Six TV Cameras at I -10 Min. G Ranger

Fig. 13-9. Artist's concept of a typical Ranger near-moon approach geometry and terminal maneuver sequence. (NASA)

exactly as directed by radio signals from earth. As the diagram shows, at launch the moon was directly opposite or above Cape Kennedy. Sixty-six hours later, the moon was thousands of miles removed from its original position when Ranger finally made its rendezvous. The control and guidance mechanism incorporated a number of technical innovations. Three-axis stabilization was achieved with an earth sensor which pointed the roll axis and solar panels at the sun and locked Ranger in pitch and yaw. Thus, the spacecraft could be programmed to any attitude for a mid-course velocity correction that would send it direct to its destination.

The Surveyor spacecraft, which is designed to make a "soft" landing on the moon and then analyze the lunar surface and transmit data back to earth, will follow the same route as Ranger. Once on the moon, the surface will be observed with television cameras, seismic activity will be monitored and local physical and chemical surface properties will be analyzed by scientists.

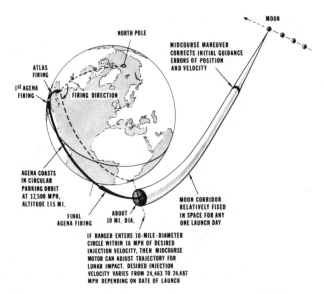

NORTH POLE

MIDCOURSE MANEUVER
CORRECTS INITIAL GUIDANCE
ERRORS OF POSITION
AND VELOCITY

MOON

ATLAS
FIRING

1st AGENA
FIRING   FIRING DIRECTION

AGENA COASTS
IN CIRCULAR
PARKING ORBIT
AT 17,500 MPH,
ALTITUDE 115 MI.

FINAL   ABOUT
AGENA FIRING   10 MI. DIA.

MOON CORRIDOR
RELATIVELY FIXED
IN SPACE FOR ANY
ONE LAUNCH DAY

IF RANGER ENTERS 10-MILE-DIAMETER
CIRCLE WITHIN 16 MPH OF DESIRED
INJECTION VELOCITY, THEN MIDCOURSE
MOTOR CAN ADJUST TRAJECTORY FOR
LUNAR IMPACT. DESIRED INJECTION
VELOCITY VARIES FROM 24,463 TO 24,487
MPH DEPENDING ON DATE OF LAUNCH

Fig. 13-10.   A typical Ranger launch to the moon. (NASA)

Fig. 13-11.   A one-eighth-inch scale model of the Surveyor spacecraft photographed in a simulated lunar atmosphere approaching the
moon for a soft landing. (NASA)

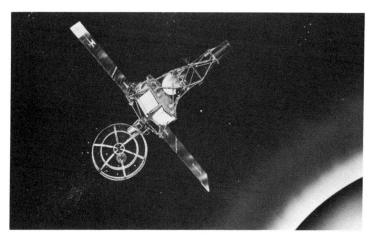

Fig. 13-12. An artist's concept of a Mariner spacecraft as it flies
by the planet Venus. (NASA)

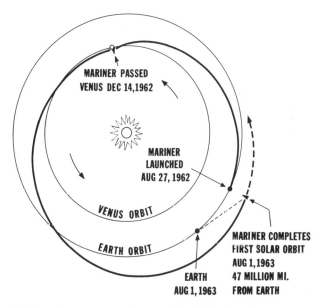

MARINER PASSED
VENUS DEC 14,1962

MARINER
LAUNCHED
AUG 27, 1962

VENUS ORBIT

EARTH ORBIT

MARINER COMPLETES
FIRST SOLAR ORBIT
AUG 1,1963
47 MILLION MI.
FROM EARTH

EARTH
AUG 1,1963

Fig. 13-13. Since launch, August 27, 1962, the Mariner II spacecraft has travelled approximately 540,000,000 miles to complete the
first solar orbit. (NASA)

Mariner II was by far one of the most successful deep space probes. Its attitude control and midcourse maneuver subsystems were functionally similar to those of the Ranger. On its 109-day, 180-million-mile flight to Venus, Mariner performed beautifully despite minor problems, including excessive temperatures, a solar-panel short circuit and a weak earth sensor signal. Mariner's mid-course maneuver corrected the Venus miss distance from about 233,000 miles to 21,000 miles. Actually, Mariner was intended to miss Venus by 10,000 miles but was designed to scan the cloud-shrouded planet effectively from as much as 40,000 miles away.

As the unmanned satellites continue to probe deeper into space, the techniques that control and guide these spacecraft to the moon, Venus, Mars and around the sun add up the sum of knowledge that man is acquiring to be used when he is finally ready to follow the robot spaceships.

14

Manned Orbiting Laboratories

Space is no longer a totally mysterious and unknown frontier. Now that manned and unmanned spacecraft have proved that man can live and function in space, the next logical step is the establishment of the orbiting space station. The interest in space stations is not new. They have intrigued men since the times of Nostradamus, Leonardo da Vinci and Jules Verne, who—each in his own way—envisioned the potential applications of space stations related to the exploration of the frontiers of space. However, what is new with respect to space stations is our recent and immediate ability to place relatively large payloads in orbit.

A manned space station placed in earth orbit to conduct additional research and to perform a wide variety of space operations will naturally lead to the two next logical steps: (1) a manned lunar base to assist in lunar exploration and exploitation, and (2) manned interplanetary flight to explore the nearest planets such as Mars and Venus. The manned space station has even been given a name—MOL for Manned Orbiting Laboratory.

One recent study proposed that a zero-gravity MOL manned by 24 scientists and astronauts could be developed and placed into orbit by 1968. Its design takes maximum advantage of zero-g; crew stations and equipment are located without regard to conventional concepts of up or down. Its operational feasibility, however, depends upon whether astronauts can survive and function properly without artificial gravity over long periods. If it is determined that they can, the zero-g concept offers important advantages in performances and design over other designs. By the time MOL would be launched, the science and techniques of remote control for spacecraft will have been perfected, as we shall now see.

The unmanned launch of building block segments of MOL would inject this cylindrical vehicle, 33 feet in diameter and 140 feet long, into an orbit 260 miles up, in a nose-toward-earth position. Huge paddle-like solar arrays then would unfold, catching the sunlight to operate the solar-cell battery power. Once aloft, this space laboratory would be ready to receive its crew, who would be launched from earth in a rendezvous flight. After docking, the men would transfer to MOL.

From the structural standpoint, its development would be relatively simple. In addition to its efficiently arranged interior and simplified structural design, its resupply requirements are fewer; it carries its own oxygen and water regenerating system, further trimming its load. The habitable portion of the space station would be pressurized to a full-time shirt-sleeve environment and would measure 70 feet in length, divided into living quarters and laboratory areas. These compartments would be separated by spherical-segment bulkheads and connected by an access tunnel running the length of the big cylinder at its core.

Although this space station is based on the *zero-g* concept, it would contain a 15-foot radius on-board centrifuge which could alleviate potential adverse effects of weightlessness on crew members. It also would precondition members for the high-g force of re-entry; it could be used for many experimental purposes, and could be of assistance in accomplishing some tasks best performed in a gravity environment, such as eating and drinking.

Working outside of MOL—in space—will be accomplished by the Modular Maneuvering Unit, a jet-propelled back pack that gives the astronaut the same steering capability as a spaceship. Its 12-nozzle propulsion system thrusts the space-suited man in any direction he wants to go. Four jets propel him forward, four backwards, two up and two down, with an attitude control system that automatically stabilizes the space-man against pitch, yaw and roll.

Of utmost importance, however, is the astronaut—the man in space. The design of space stations and their subsequent use depend upon the human factors involved. Can man *really* live and function for long periods of time in space? A manned orbiting laboratory will answer this question, for the space station is an essential and necessary component to the success of manned interplanetary flight. If it develops that man has serious physiological limitations, the space station could provide unique facilities and capabilities to investigate and determine criteria and solutions to allow man to overcome his limitation, and permit him to perform essential functions effectively and efficiently for the long periods necessary for successful manned planetary flight missions.

Personnel at the space station could investigate and establish the environmental criteria, such as radiation, meteoroids, and the other combined factors of the operational space environment which must be provided for in the design and development of the planetary spacecraft.

The space station could provide support for planetary flights, by conducting research on plants, animals, materials, finishes, processes, and equipment in the operational space environment.

Another area of potential space station contributions to the planetary program is the use of proven, tested, qualified building-block segments containing the basic structure, airlocks, and subsystems for the man-occupied part of the planetary spacecraft.

The space station could be instrumental in developing the crew qualifications for the planetary mission by providing the facilities for crew selection in the operational space environment and in the complete training of a competent, experienced crew prior to initiation of the mission.

The planetary mission may require an orbital launch operations facility. The space station will provide accommodations for the launch operations crew, and a base for shops and equipment necessary for the assembly and checkout of the payload segments of the planetary spacecraft in earth orbit.

The role of the space station in the lunar base program is very similar in many ways to that described for the planetary mission.

First of all, the lunar base crew could be selected and trained in the station, based on information obtained from the Apollo manned landings on the lunar surface. The crew could be subjected to lunar gravity levels and other conditions for long durations, by simulating lunar surface conditions in the near earth-orbital environment, which cannot be duplicated on earth.

At least certain elements of the lunar base could be built from the proven, tested, qualified building-block segments of the space station, precluding the expensive design and development of completely new facilities for manned occupancy on the moon. The previously qualified subsystems of the station could be utilized, or new, more specially required adaptations could be developed and qualified in a true simulation of the lunar environment prior to transportation and activations on the lunar surface.

With respect to the lunar-base logistics transportation system, the space station could receive payloads from earth which could be stored and prepared for trans-shipment to the moon.

The orbital-launch-operations facilities, essentially the same as those used for the planetary mission, also could be used to support the lunar-base-logistics operations. The logistics transportation shuttle could be serviced, maintained, repaired, and overhauled at the space station with the facilities available there. In case of emergency, rescue missions might be initiated more quickly, and flexibly from earth orbit than from earth's surface.

In the general advance of science and technology to support the exploration of space, the space station could make unparalleled contributions not possible on earth or by current space flight programs now under development.

The space station could be a national research facility in the operational space environment to conduct all types of basic and applied scientific research to further man's advances in space. In the accomplishment of such activities, much valuable data on the space environment could also be collected to establish design criteria for future programs.

Scientific probes could be launched to obtain data to meet the requirements specified by other programs.

Proposed advances in propulsion systems could be researched and qualified for future use, particularly where testing is not physically or economically practical on earth.

Another area of research where only the space station could provide effective facilities is in long term investigations of biological, physiological, psychological, hereditary, and genetic factors related to man, animals, and plants.

The infinite vacuum of space is available to the space station to be utilized in experiments, or possibly in commercial applications requiring the attainment of very hard vacuum of unlimited capacity.

In reviewing and analyzing space station capabilities, it should be realized that the capability to develop the space station and to achieve these objectives is now available. The technology to develop the space station is in existence, but it is still necessary to exercise the utmost ingenuity and intelligence in planning and designing the space station to achieve maximum results. The feasibility of the space station has been demonstrated by numerous studies, and the required technology in many ways is less demanding than that required for Project Apollo, for example, with its complex navigation and guidance, reentry heat protection, propulsion subsystems, and lunar landing devices.

There are many other non-scientific uses foreseen for orbiting space stations. One important military and political function would be to help maintain international peace and security by the constant observation of the earth for information about military preparations. One of the great problems in today's world is the uncertainty generated by the secret development, testing, and deployment of national armaments and by the lack of information on military preparations within closed societies. If in fact a nation is not preparing surprise attack, observations from space could help us to know this and thereby increase confidence in world security which might otherwise be subject to added and unnecessary doubts.

Observations from space may in time provide support of

arms control and disarmament arrangements, although they could not eliminate the need for ground inspection. Of perhaps greater significance is the fact that the progress of science decrees that we are all to live in an increasingly open world.

It is obvious from any discussion of observation in space that there is no workable dividing line between military and non-military uses. Weather satellites are of significance to the armed forces, just as they are important to civilian populations. Similarly, heat-sensing devices aboard earth satellites might be developed to detect not only the heat from forest fires, but also the heat generated in the launching of ballistic missiles.

In respect of the impossibility of decisively separating the military and non-military applications, observation of the earth from space is not different from other uses of space. A navigational satellite can guide a war vessel as well as a merchant ship. A communications satellite can serve a military establishment as well as civilian communities. The instruments which guide a space vehicle on a scientific mission may also guide a space vehicle on a military mission.

As we have seen, the future of the manned orbiting space station or laboratory is of vast importance to many nations, now that man has extended himself into space. The MOL will be a vital part of this, the Space Age.

15

What Will be Next?

What comes after the moon?

The answer to this question is as complex as man's boundless imagination. Although we have yet to land men on the moon, scientists are giving a great deal of thought to what comes next in space. The control, guidance and navigation of spacecraft will be refined and improved upon while man establishes himself on the moon in lunar frontier bases.

Obviously, then, the further exploration of the planets in our solar system will come next. Although, a mission to Mars or Venus will in some areas duplicate the flight to the moon, there will also be some differences. In a flight from the earth to the moon, for example, the earth assumes the dominant role. In a flight to Mars or Venus, the sun assumes the dominant role because a spaceship cast on a free orbit toward another planet—remember, the moon is a satellite of the earth, not a true planet orbiting the sun—actually becomes an independent member of the solar system travelling an ellipse relative to the sun.

One important difference between an interplanetary flight and a moon flight is that the interplanetary traveller can make use of the earth's orbital velocity. When a spaceship is en route to the moon, both ship and moon—because they are part of the earth system in space—travel with the earth as it moves around the sun. In such an arrangement, there is no way for the ship to take advantage of the earth's motion in its orbit.

If an interplanetary vehicle leaves the earth in the general direction of the earth's forward movement, however, its initial speed relative to the rest of the solar system will include the orbital speed of the earth, 66,000 miles per hour.

To effect this maneuver, the vehicle accelerates—from either
the earth's surface or a circular orbit—along a globe-girdling
curve calculated to reach escape velocity when the craft is
moving parallel to the earth's orbit. At this point it needs no
further increase in speed to enter the elliptical curve around
the sun.

The "free lift" supplied by the earth's motion is particularly
useful when the destination is a planet whose orbit lies outside that of the earth, such as Mars, Jupiter, or Saturn. For a
trip to our nearest "inner" planet, Venus, or for a return trip
from Mars to Earth, full orbital velocity is not needed.

The earth, it will be recalled, travels at the exact speed required to balance the sun's gravity. So if a space traveller
wants to move toward the sun—which is what he must do
when "dropping" from an outer planet to an inner one—he
must first cancel some of the orbital speed of the outer planet.

One way to do this is to time a rocket's departure so it
attains escape velocity while travelling counter to the earth's
motion around the sun. Thus it will have "escaped" the earth
and yet will be moving at a speed less than the earth's orbital
speed, hence will begin "falling" toward the orbit of Venus.

Whether the goal is an inner orbit or an outer one, the most
economical method of transfer is to apply a minimum of
power at departure and arrival, "coasting" through the greater
part of the journey. Such interplanetary flight paths are called
minimum energy orbits or tangential ellipses.

Transfer times for minimum energy orbits are long. Some
259 days are required for passage to Mars, 146 days for Venus.

The space traveler also faces a long wait on other planets
before orbital positions are favorable for return to Earth. On
Mars the waiting period is 455 days, which, coupled with
flight time both ways, amounts to 973 days (about 2 years,
8 months) for the total mission. The waiting period on Venus
is 465 days, giving a total of 757 days for the round trip.

More direct routes to the planets, plus reduced waiting
periods, will be possible as greater propulsive power becomes
available. Shorter, more direct elliptical flight paths will then
be used. With unlimited power, a ship might cross to Mars

when Earth and Mars are at opposition (passing each other on the same side of the sun).

High-energy routes will be essential for missions beyond the orbit of Mars in order to keep total mission time at reasonable levels.

The method by which a spaceship lands on a planet or moon depends on atmospheric conditions. If an atmosphere is present, frictional braking plus use of wing surfaces is possible. If not, rocket power must supply the braking force.

The chief advantage of using an atmosphere to reduce velocity is the saving in extra propellant weight. A large rocket engine operating as little as 10 seconds consumes liquid propellant weighing thousands of pounds, and every unnecessary pound carried subtracts from over-all velocity and range.

In frictional braking, a vehicle deliberately "brushes" the outer part of the atmosphere on its first approach. This brief encounter, which must be performed with great accuracy to avoid excessive heating, slows the ship somewhat and sends it into a long ellipse around the planet and back into the atmosphere again, this time—because kinetic energy was converted into heat in the first meeting—at a lower altitude. The process is repeated five or six times, the ellipse contracting as the ship penetrates deeper into the atmosphere. Heat generated in each entry is dissipated by radiation in the subsequent swing through space.

Finally, speed is reduced sufficiently to allow a landing through use of wings, parachute or small bursts of power. A ship can also combine frictional braking with short rocket firings designed to create a temporary orbit about a planet.

Powered deceleration into a circular or elliptic orbit is less risky than atmospheric braking, and permits closer control of the position and shape of the final orbit. If it is necessary to turn the ship before applying power, this is easily accomplished by firing small side rockets or spinning a flywheel mounted in the ship.

The same maneuver can be used if the ship is to decelerate all or most of the way to the surface of a body having no atmosphere.

Space vehicles on deep space probes will either have ground control, on board control or no control beyond the attempt to achieve proper aim and speed at rocket engine burnout.

The latter technique—the ballistic launch—is less than adequate, due to high sensitivity to perturbations. Not only is extreme accuracy at burnout required, but so is vastly improved knowledge of such astronomical factors as the true distance of the planets from the sun, the mass of the earth-moon system and the orbital characteristics of all bodies in our region of space.

For example, a rocket being launched to Venus will miss the planet if its burnout velocity deviates more than five-tenths of a foot per second from the necessary 37,000 feet per second. Such accuracy is not yet feasible.

Remote operation of a spaceship's rockets from ground transmitters is possible, although this requires constant tracking of the ship's flight path by electronic or optical means. Tracking over astronomical distances with the required accuracy is very difficult, and should be supplemented by onboard guidance.

Onboard guidance, moreover, is needed for close approaches to or landings on other worlds. An onboard system requires complete facilities for star navigation, special navigational equipment for approach to planets, and side rockets or internal flywheels for attitude control.

The problem is further complicated by the fact that the solar system has but one fixed point, the sun. This means the space navigator must recognize that any point of departure and any point of arrival will be in motion.

Experience cannot always be the guide. No two shots to another world can ever be the same, even for identical vehicles. The positions of potentially perturbing bodies would never be the same. The distance separating the two planets would rarely be the same.

Calculation of exact interplanetary flight paths is therefore a matter for electronic computers. The overwhelming distances between the solar system and other star systems demand a space flight technology far beyond that foreseeable at the present time. If we were to travel to Proxima Centauri, the nearest star, it would take us 1,200 years to get there even if we were moving at a speed of 223,200 miles per hour, or nearly nine times the velocity required to "escape" the earth's gravitational pull. Light, travelling 186,000 miles per second, requires 4½ years to cover the distance.

To even attempt space flight to another solar system will require a major quantum jump in our space flight technology. It is even obvious that nuclear power will not suffice. We would need some kind of a propulsion system that can completely transform matter into energy, according to Einstein's famous equation relating to the mixing of electrons with positrons and radiating the entire matter away. Scientists do not know how to accomplish this at the present time, but it is this kind of speed-of-light energy that is required to travel to the stars.

Meanwhile, we are making studies in engine propulsion techniques that may lead to this quantum jump sometime in the distant future. Chemical combustion is now used in rocket propulsion because no other means of accelerating mass to high exhaust speeds has been perfected. Other, more promising systems under study include:

Nuclear Fission. In this power plant, the enormous heat energy of atomic fission is used to help create an exhaust thrust. Heat itself does not produce thrust, but a nuclear reactor can be used to heat some substance which, when channeled through a nozzle in conventional rocket engine fashion, produces a reaction. Among substances suggested as the "working fluid" are liquid hydrogen, helium and ammonia.

Performance of a nuclear rocket would be limited by the energy content of the working fluid and temperature limitations of reactor materials. Specific impulse estimates for nuclear rockets range from 600 to 1,500 seconds.

Rocket engineers doubt that we will be able to achieve thrust through direct exhaustion of nuclear fission particles.

Nuclear Fusion. The fusion rocket would use the force of the H-bomb, the energy created in the uniting or fusing of the lightest atomic nuclei into heavier nuclei. A likely fuel would be deuterium, a form of hydrogen, which is readily available in oceans and hence a better long-term fuel than the uranium used in atomic fission.

Heating deuterium to very high temperatures would create a high speed plasma (hot gas) capable of specific impulse ratings in the millions of seconds. It is estimated that temperatures around 350 million degrees would be needed to sustain a fusion reaction. Since solid walls would not stand up under such conditions, it has been proposed that exhaust masses be contained by magnetic fields shaped as nozzles.

Before fusion can be applied to rocket propulsion, however, scientists must learn how to control fusion energy in the laboratory.

Ion Power. Ions (atoms unbalanced electrically by the removal of one or more electrons) are accelerated to high speeds by electrical fields. The ions can be formed by passing a "propellant" through an ionizing device. The source of electrical energy can be a nuclear reactor, batteries, or a solar radiation system. Exhaust velocities would be very high, but due to the low mass of ion particles, the ion rocket would have relatively little thrust and therefore would not be suitable for surface launch when strong gravity must be overcome. Chemical or nuclear rockets could boost ion vehicles into space, or the vehicles could be assembled and launched in orbit.

Arc Heating. An electrical arc is used to heat a working fluid which is expelled through a nozzle. Energy for the arc must be derived from a nuclear reactor, batteries or solar radiation.

Solar Power. Sunlight is converted to heat energy, which is then used to expand a fluid such as liquid hydrogen. Thrust values would be low, but several hundred times higher than those of an ion or fusion system.

Photon Power. A beam of light exerts pressure. Thus very high radiation of photons (light particles) could provide sufficient thrust to move a vehicle in space. Again, the low mass of photons would result in low thrust and low acceleration, but particle velocities would be 186,000 miles per second, the speed of all electromagnetic energy. Theoretically, then, a photon-powered vehicle could attain a speed close to that of light. However, no method of radiating tremendously intense beams of light is known.

Venus is our closest neighboring planet, but landing on its cloud-blanketed surface is out of the question at this time. The surface of Venus is too hot for humans. The only visit to Venus now foreseen is a manned flight that will orbit close to the surface of this planet without landing. Mars is a more likely prospect.

The question of life on other worlds has long fascinated man and now, for the first time, he may be on the threshold of learning the answer. Although Mariner flew past Venus and provided some clues as to whether life exists there, it will not be until instruments can be landed on the planets that conclusive answers may be had.

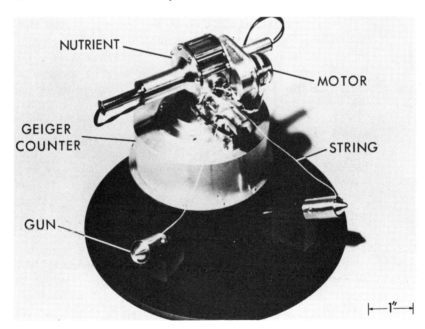

Fig. 15-1. Internal mechanism of the unmanned exploration space-craft "Gulliver" designed to detect life on planet Mars. (NASA)

In fact, the question, "After the moon what?" can be answered simply: Mars!

Naturally, the first spacecraft from Earth to visit Mars will be unmanned. It may be called "Gulliver." This is an unmanned exploration spacecraft designed to go fishing on Mars. The tackle will consist of three "sticky strings" dropped out of a porthole. As the strings are reeled in they will retrieve living organisms—if any—in the soil. Gulliver will "cook" the prey on the spot. If Gulliver catches anything, it will radio the news to Earth after it digests the results of its fishing expedition.

Gulliver will weigh approximately three-fourths of a pound. When it lands on Mars, small ports will open in the capsule wall and projectiles will be fired. They will carry the strings out about 50 feet. Once inside the capsule, soil particles picked by the sticky strings will be doused with a sterile broth tagged with radioisotopes.

Should the Martian soil contain any living organisms they should begin to grow within four hours and produce a radioactive gas inside Gulliver. This gas will be detected by a transistorized Geiger counter. Thus, it may be a series of clicking noises radioed across the reaches of space which tell men on Earth of life on another world.

The manned spaceship to Mars which may make its flight by 1975 might carry quite a bit of "excess baggage." The astronauts won't mind having it around, however, for they couldn't get home without it. This excess baggage may be a spaceship made up of portions of a blunter circular cone and an elliptic cone, fitted together. This odd vehicle will do nothing much but go along for the ride for most of the approximate 400-day mission.

For the final eight hours of this return flight, however—near approach to the earth, reentry into the earth's atmosphere and the landing on *terra firma*—it comes alive. In fact, its performance determines whether the mission succeeds or fails. Its job is to carry four to six astronauts to a safe earth landing. To do this, it must withstand high heating rates generated by a fantastic earth-atmosphere entry speed, and heavy

Fig. 15-2. After being landed on Mars, Gulliver shoots the strings out. Organisms caught by a sticky substance on the strings are reeled in. Their life activity, if any, would be recorded by a Geiger counter and radioed to Earth from Gulliver. (NASA)

external pressure loads. Further, it must be able to land in a pre-determined area. The design of such a vehicle represents a new concept in reentry vehicle configuration.

Reentry speeds up to 65,000 feet per second have to be considered for a return from a 1975 Mars mission! By comparison, the Mercury spacecraft entered the earth's atmosphere at only 26,000 feet per second. Apollo flights will be subjected to the slightly higher rate of 36,000 feet per second. Thus, earth reentry heating rates will be very high. Air temperatures can be as high as 20,000 degrees centigrade, compared to the sun's surface temperature of 6,000 degrees!

Protection from this heat will come from a shield of ablating material of advanced design. This material, about three and one-half inches thick, will absorb the incoming heat by "burning off" of the front cone. It will thus hold the main structure to a safe temperature of about 300 degrees.

Behind the heat shield will be the main shell, a stainless steel sandwich. The inner skin of the sandwich will be a pressure vessel to withstand high external loads as well as pressure from an internal atmosphere. The forebody, or main heat shield, is a blunted circular cone, raked off at a suitable angle. Together the cones enclose a 500-cubic-foot volume. The afterbody is an elliptic cone. The re-entry vehicle is de-

Fig. 15-3. Extended Apollo concepts will be useful as an early space station because of its great flexibility for returning cargo and also since it is designed for higher re-entry speed, it will be useful for exploration to higher orbits than could be accomplished with a Gemini B. (NASA)

signed for parachute recover, as in the Apollo series, and surface landing. Emergency water landing also could be made.

Perceptible atmosphere will be entered at about 400,000 feet altitude, at an entry angle of approximately seven degrees. The vehicle will pull out of its trajectory at about 200,000 feet, and decelerate in level flight. At this point, reaction jets—actually rockets—will control the vehicle's attitude. Maneuvering will be done by rolling the vehicle to control the direction of the lifting force. This will allow selection of widely separated, alternate landing sites. For example, a down-range flight of 16,000 nautical miles may be achieved, with a cross-range movement of 1,000 nautical miles. This means that if the original landing site had been in California's Mojave desert, the alternate landing point could be as far away as Woomera, Australia!

A trip to Mars staggers the imagination. At the turn of this century, a trip anywhere on earth also staggered the imagination. In the year 2,000 A.D., flights to the moon may be commonplace, but there will still be opportunities for exploration in endless space. Man, who once feared to venture beyond his familiar landmarks, is now controlling, guiding and navigating his spaceships through space—the last frontier.

Glossary

Acceleration. The rate of change of velocity.

Accelerometer. An instrument which measures acceleration or gravitational forces capable of imparting acceleration.

Acquisition. 1. The process of locating the orbit of a satellite or trajectory of a space probe so that tracking or telemetry data can be gathered. 2. The process of pointing an antenna or telescope so that it is properly oriented to allow gathering of tracking or telemetry data from a satellite or space probe.

Aerodynamics. The science that treats of the motion of air and other gaseous fluids, and of the forces acting on bodies when the bodies move through such fluids, or when such fluids move against or around the bodies as 'his research in aerodynamics.'

Aerodynamic vehicle. A device, such as an airplane, glider, etc., capable of flight only within a sensible atmosphere and relying on aerodynamic forces to maintain flight.

Aerospace. (From *aero*nautics and *space*.) Of or pertaining to both the earth's atmosphere and space, as in 'aerospace industries.'

Aerothermodynamic border. An altitude at about 100 miles, above which the atmosphere is so rarefied that the motion of an object through it at high speeds generates no significant surface heat.

Ailerons. Hinged control surfaces along the outer trailing edges of a wing, which operate in an up-and-down motion. They enable the pilot to maneuver through banks and to perform turns and other maneuvers.

Airfoil. A wing.

Analog computer. A computing machine that works on the principle of measuring, as distinguished from counting, in which the input data are made analogous to a measurement continuum, such as voltages, linear lengths, resistances, light intensities, etc., which can be manipulated by the computer. Analog computers range from the relatively simple devices of the slide rule or airspeed indicator to complicated electrical machines used for solving mathematical problem.

Aphelion. The point at which a planet or other celestial object in orbit about the sun is farthest from the sun.

Apogee. In an orbit about the earth, the point at which the satellite is farthest from the earth; the highest altitude reached by a sounding rocket.

Apogee rocket. A rocket attached to a satellite or spacecraft designed to fire when the craft is at apogee, the point farthest from the earth in orbit. The effect of the apogee rocket is to establish a new orbit farther from the earth or to allow the craft to escape from earth orbit.

Arc-jet engine. A type of electrical rocket engine in which the propellant gas is heated by passing through an electrical arc.

Artificial gravity. A simulated gravity established within a space vehicle, as by rotating a cabin about an axis of a spacecraft, the centrifugal force generated being similar to the force of gravity.

Astro. A prefix meaning 'star' or 'stars' and, by extension, sometimes used as the equivalent of 'celestial,' as in *astro*nautics.

Astroballistics. The study of the phenomena arising out of the motion of a solid through a gas at speeds high enough to cause ablation; for example, the interaction of a meteoroid with the atmosphere.

Astrodynamics. The practical application of celestial mechanics, astroballistics, propulsion theory, and allied fields to the problem of planning and directing the trajectories of space vehicles.

Astronaut. A person who occupies a space vehicle. Specifically one of the test pilots selected to participate in Projects Mercury, Gemini, and Apollo, the first United States program for manned space flight.

Astronautics. The art, skill, or activity of operating space vehicles. In a broader sense, the science of space flight.

Astronomical unit. In the astronomical system of measures, a unit of length usually defined as the distance from the earth to the sun, approximately 92,900,000 statute miles or 149,600,000 kilometers.

Attitude. The position or orientation of an aircraft, spacecraft, etc., either in motion or at rest, as determined by the relationship between its axes and some reference line or plane such as the horizon.

Axis. (pl. axes) A straight line about which a body rotates, or around which a plane figure may rotate to produce a solid; a line of symmetry. One of a set of reference lines for certain systems of coordinates.

Azimuth. Horizontal direction or bearing.

Backup. An item kept available to replace an item which fails to perform satisfactorily. An item under development intended to perform the same general function performed by another item also under development.

Ballistics. The science that deals with the motion, behavior, and effects of projectiles, especially bullets, aerial bombs, rockets, or the like; the science or art of designing and hurling projectiles so as to achieve a desired performance.

Ballistic trajectory. The trajectory followed by a body being acted upon only by gravitational forces and the resistance of the medium through which it passes. A rocket without lifting surfaces is in a ballistic trajectory after its engines cease operating.

Beam. A ray or collection of focused rays of radiated energy. Radio waves used as a navigation aid.

Beam-rider. A craft following a beam, particularly one which does so automatically, the beam providing the guidance.

Bipropellant. A rocket propellant consisting of two unmixed or uncombined chemicals (fuel and oxidizer) fed to the combustion chamber separately.

Bird. A colloquial term for a rocket, satellite, or spacecraft.

Black box. Colloquially, any unit, usually an electronic device such as an amplifier, which can be mounted in a rocket, spacecraft, or the like as a single package.

Blockhouse. A reinforced concerte structure, often built underground or partly underground, and sometimes dome-shaped, to provide protection against blast, heat, or explosion during rocket launchings or related activities; specifically, such a structure at a launch site that houses electronic control instruments used in launching a rocket.

Boiloff. The vaporization of a cold propellant such as liquid oxygen or liquid hydrogen, as the temperature of the propellant mass rises as in the tank of a rocket being readied for launch.

Booster. Short for 'booster engine' or 'booster rocket.'

Booster engine. An engine, especially a booster rocket, that adds its thrust to the thrust of the sustainer engine.

Booster rocket. A rocket engine, either solid or liquid fuel, that assists the normal propulsive system or sustainer engine of a rocket or aeronautical vehicle in some phase of its flight. A rocket used to set a missile vehicle in motion before another engine takes over.

Burn. A period during which a rocket engine is firing, as in 'second burn,' the second period during a flight in which the engine is firing.

Burnout. An act or instance of the end of fuel and oxidizer burning in a rocket; the time at which this burnout occurs.

Celestial mechanics. The study of the theory of the motions of celestial bodies under the influence of gravitational fields.

Center of gravity. Aircraft, ships, submarines, and rocket boosters have three axes about which all motion takes place. The longitudinal axis runs from nose to tail, the lateral axis is perpendicular to the other two. The center of gravity is where all three axes meet, and where perfect balance of the vehicle is achieved.

Centrifuge. Specifically, a large motor-driven apparatus with a long arm at the end of which human and animal subjects or equipment can be revolved and rotated at various speeds to simulate very closely the prolonged accelerations encountered in high-performance aircraft, rockets, and spacecraft.

Checkout. A sequence of actions taken to test or examine a launch vehicle or spacecraft as to its readiness to perform its intended function.

Chemical fuel. A fuel that depends upon an oxidizer for combustion or for development of thrust, such as liquid or solid rocket fuel or internal-combustion-engine fuel; distinguished from nuclear fuel.

Chemical rocket. A rocket using chemical fuel, fuel which requires an oxidizer for combustion, such as liquid or solid rocket fuel.

Cislunar. Of or pertaining to phenomena, projects, or activity in the space between the earth and moon, or between the earth and the moon's orbit.

Command. A signal which initiates or triggers an action in the device which receives the signal.

Communications satellite. A satellite designed to reflect or relay radio or other communications waves.

Complex. Entire area of launch site facilities. This includes blockhouse, launch pad, gantry, etc. Also referred to as a 'launch complex.'

Computer. A machine for carrying out calculations and performing specified transformations on information.

Configuration. A particular type of a specific aircraft, rocket, etc., which differs from others of the same model by virtue of the arrangement of its components or by the addition or omission of auxiliary equipment as 'long-range configuration,' 'cargo configuration.'

Console. An array of controls and indicators for the monitoring and control of a particular sequence of actions, as in the checkout of a rocket, a countdown action, or a launch procedure. A console is usually designed around desklike arrays. It permits the operator to monitor and control different activating instruments, data recording instruments, or event sequencers.

Control. Specifically, to direct the movements of an aircraft, rocket, or spacecraft with particular reference to changes in altitude and speed.

Control rocket. A vernier engine, retrorocket, or other such rocket, used to guide or make small changes in the velocity of a rocket, spacecraft, or the like.

Cosmic rays. The extremely high-energy subatomic particles which bombard the atmosphere from outer space. Cosmic-ray primaries seem to be mostly protons, hydrogen nuclei, but also comprise heavier nuclei. On colliding with atmospheric particles they produce many different kinds of lower-energy secondary cosmic radiation.

Countdown. The time period in which a sequence of events is carried out to launch a rocket; the sequence of events.

Cutoff. An act or instance of shutting something off; specifically in rocketry, an act or instance of shutting off the propellant flow in a rocket, or of stopping the combustion of the propellant.

Deceleration. The act or process of moving, or of causing to move, with decreasing speed; the state of so moving.

Deep space probes. Spacecraft designed for exploring space to the vicinity of the moon and beyond. Deep space probes with specific missions may be referred to as 'lunar probe,' 'Mars probe,' 'solar probe,' etc.

Digital computer. A computer which operates on the principle of counting as opposed to measuring. See analog computer.

Docking. The process of bringing two spacecraft together while in space.

Drag. The force represented by the resistance of the air to a body moving through air, or the resistance of water to a ship or submarine moving through water.

Drogue parachute. A type of parachute attached to a body, used to slow it down; also called 'deceleration parachute,' or 'drag parachute.'

Eccentric. Not having the same center; varying from a circle, as in 'eccentric orbit.'

Ecliptic. The apparent annual path of the sun among the stars; the intersection of the plane of the earth's orbit with the celestial sphere.

Electric propulsion. The generation of thrust for a rocket engine involving acceleration of a propellant by some electrical device such as an arc jet, ion engine, or magnetohydrodynamic accelerator.

Electronic data processing. The use of electronic devices and systems in the processing of data so as to interpret the data and put it into usable form.

Elevators. Hinged control surfaces attached to the horizontal stabilizer of an aircraft or submarine. The movement of the elevators to an up-or-down position will force the tail of an aircraft or the stern of a submarine to change its attitude and either climb or dive. In the case of an airplane, the elevators change the angle of attach of the wing, thus determining the amount of lift produced by the wing.

Ellipse. A plane curve constituting the locus of all points the sum of whose distances from two fixed points called 'foci' is constant; an elongated circle.

Escape velocity. The radial speed which a particular or larger body must attain in order to escape from the gravitational field of a planet or star. The escape velocity from Earth is approximately 7 miles per sec.; from Mars, 3.2 miles per sec.; and from the Sun, 390 miles per sec. In order for a celestial body to retain an atmosphere for astronomically long periods of time, the mean velocity of the atmospheric molecules must be considerably below the escape velocity.

Explosive bolt. A bolt incorporating an explosive which can be detonated on command, thus destroying the bolt. Explosive bolts are used, for example, in separating a satellite from a rocket.

Extraterrestrial. From outside the earth.

Fallaway section. A section of a rocket vehicle that is cast off and separates from the vehicle during flight, especially such a section that falls back to the earth.

Fixed satellite. An earth satellite that orbits from west to east at such a speed as to remain constantly over a given place in the earth's equator.

Flare. A bright eruption from the sun's chromosphere. Flares may appear within minutes and fade within an hour. They cover a wide range of intensity and size, and they tend to occur between sunspots. Flares are related to radio fadeouts and terrestrial magnetic disturbances.

Free fall. The fall or drop of a body, such as a rocket, not guided, not under thrust, and not retarded by a parachute or other braking device. Weightlessness.

Fuselage. The main body of an airplane, to which are attached the engine and propeller, wings, tail, and landing gear.

g or G. An acceleration equal to the acceleration of gravity, approximately 32.2 feet per second at sea level; used as a unit of stress measurement for bodies undergoing acceleration.

Gimbal. A device with two mutually perpendicular and intersecting axes of rotation, thus giving free angular movement in two directions, on which an engine or other object may be mounted. In a gyro, a support which provides the spin axis with a degree-of-freedom.

Gravitation. The acceleration produced by the mutual attraction of two masses, directed along the line joining their centers of mass, and of magnitude inversely proportional to the square of the distance between the two centers of mass.

Gravity. The force imparted by the earth to a mass on or close to the earth. Since the earth is rotating, the force observed as gravity is the resultant of the force of gravitation and the centrifugal force arising from this rotation.

Guidance. The process of directing the movements of an aeronautical vehicle or space vehicle, with particular reference to the selection of a flight path or trajectory.

Gyro. A device which utilizes the angular momentum of a spinning rotor to sense angular motion of its base about one or two axes at right angles to the spin axis. Also called 'gyroscope.'

Impact area. The area in which a rocket strikes the earth's surface.

Inertial guidance. Guidance by means of acceleration measured and integrated within the craft.

Injection. The process of putting an artificial satellite into orbit. Also the time of such action.

Intercontinental ballistic missile (ICBM). A ballistic missile with a range of 5,000 miles or more.

Ion. An atom or molecularly bound group of atoms having an electric charge. Sometimes also a free electron or other charged subatomic particle.

Launch pad. The load-bearing base or platform from which a rocket vehicle is launched. Usually called 'pad.'

Launch vehicle. Any device which propels and guides a spacecraft into orbit about the earth or into a trajectory to another celestial body. Often called 'booster.'

Launch window. An interval of time during which a rocket can be launched to accomplish a particular purpose as 'lift-off occurred 5 minutes after the beginning of the 82-minute launch window.'

Lift. The difference in air pressure between the upper and lower surfaces of a wing, providing an upward lifting force.

Lift-off. The action of a rocket vehicle as it separates from its launch pad in a vertical ascent.

Liquid-propellant rocket engine. A rocket engine fueled with a propellant or propellants in liquid form. Also called 'liquid-propellant rocket.' Rocket engines of this kind vary somewhat in complexity, but they consist essentially of one or more combustion chambers together with the necessary pipes, valves, pumps, injectors, etc.

Longitudinal axis. The fore-and-aft line through the center of gravity of a craft.

Lox. 1. Liquid oxygen. Used attributively as in 'lox tank,' 'lox unit.' Also called 'loxygen.' 2. To load the fuel tanks of a rocket vehicle with liquid oxygen. Hence, 'loxing.'

Main stage. In a multistage rocket, the stage that develops the greatest amount of thrust, with or without booster engines. In a single-stage rocket vehicle powered by one or more engines, the period when full thrust (at or above 90 percent) is attained. A sustainer engine, considered as a stage after booster engines have fallen away, as in 'the main stage of the Atlas.'

Mass. The measure of the amount of matter in a body; its inertia. The weight of a body is the force with which it is attracted by the earth.

Missile. Any object thrown, dropped, fired, launched, or otherwise projected with the purpose of striking a target. Short for 'ballistic missile,' 'guided missile.'

Module. A self-contained unit of a launch vehicle or spacecraft which serves as a building block for the overall structure. The module is usually designated by its primary function as 'command module,' 'lunar landing module,' etc. A one-package assembly of functionally associated electronic parts; usually a plug-in unit.

Multistage rocket. A vehicle having two or more rocket units, each unit firing after the one in back of it has exhausted its propellant. Normally, each unit, or stage, is jettisoned after completing its firing. Also called a 'multiple-stage rocket' or, infrequently, a 'step rocket.'

Newton's law of motion. A set of three fundamental postulates forming the basis of the mechanics of rigid bodies, formulated by Newton in 1687. The first law is concerned with the principle of inertia and states that if a body in motion is not acted upon by an external force, its momentum remains constant (law of conservation of momentum). The second law asserts that the rate of change of momentum of a body is proportional to the force acting upon the body and is in the direction of the applied force.

Nozzle. Specifically, the part of a rocket thrust chamber assembly in which the gases produced in the chamber are accelerated to high velocities.

Nuclear fuel. Fissionable material of reasonably long life, used or usable in producing energy in a nuclear reactor.

Nuclear reactor. An apparatus in which nuclear fission may be sustained in a self-supporting chain reaction. Commonly called 'reactor.'

Orbit. The path of a body or particle under the influence of a gravitational or other force. For instance, the orbit of a celestial body is its path relative to another body around which it revolves. To go around the earth or other body in an orbit.

Orbital period. The interval between successive passages of a satellite.

Orbital velocity. The average velocity at which an earth satellite or other orbiting body travels around its primary. The velocity of such a body at any given point in its orbit, as in 'its orbital velocty at the apogee is less than at the perigee.'

Paraglider. A flexible-winged, kitelike vehicle designed for use in a recovery system for launch vehicles or as a reentry vehicle.

Passive. Reflecting a signal without transmission, as 'Echo is a passive satellite.' Contrasted with 'active.'

Payload. Originally, the revenue-producing portion of an aircraft's load, e.g., passengers, cargo, mail, etc. By extension, that which an aircraft, rocket, or the like carries over and above what is necessary for the operation of the vehicle during its flight.

Peri. A prefix meaning near, as in 'perigee.'

Perigee. That orbital point nearest the earth when the earth is the center of attraction. That orbital point farthest from the earth is called 'apogee.' Perigee and apogee are used by many writers in referring to orbits of satellites, thus avoiding coinage of new terms for each planet and moon.

Photon. According to the quantum theory of radiation, the elementary quantity, or 'quantum,' of radiant energy.

Photon engine. A projected type of reaction engine in which thrust would be obtained from a stream of electromagnetic radiation. Although the thrust of this engine would be minute, it may be possible to apply it for extended periods of time. Theoretically, in space, where no resistance is offered by air particles, very high speeds may build up.

Plasma. An electrically conductive gas comprised of neutral particles, ionized particles, and free electrons but which, taken as a whole, is electrically neutral.

Plasma engine. A reaction engine using magnetically accelerated plasma as propellant. A plasma engine is a type of electrical engine.

Plasma jet. A magnetohydrodynamic rocket engine in which the ejection of plasma generates thrust.

Posigrade rocket. An auxiliary rocket which fires in the direction in which the vehicle is pointed, used for example in separating two stages of a vehicle.

Precession. The change in the direction of the axis of rotation of a spinning body or of the plane of the orbit of an orbiting body when acted upon by an outside force.

Precession of the equinoxes. The conical motion of the earth's axis about the vertical to the plane of the ecliptic, caused by the attractive force of the sun, moon, and other planets on the equatorial proturberance of the earth.

Probe. Any device inserted in an environment for the purpose of obtaining information about the environment, specifically, an instrumented vehicle moving through the upper atmosphere or space, or landing upon another celestial body in order to obtain information about the specific environment.

Propellant. Short for 'rocket propellant.'

Quatum theory. The theory (first stated by Max Planck before the Physical Society of Berlin on December 14, 1900) that all electromagnetic radiation is emitted and absorbed in 'quanta' each of magnitude hv, h being Planck's constant and v the radiation.

Reaction control system. A system of controlling the attitude of a craft when outside the atmosphere by using jets of gas in lieu of aerodynamic control surfaces.

Reaction engine. An engine that develops thrust by its reaction to ejection of a substance from it; specifically, such an engine that ejects a jet or stream of gases created by the burning of fuel within the engine. A reaction engine operates in accordance with Newton's third law of motion, i.e., to every action (force) there is an equal and opposite reaction. Both rocket engines and jet engines are reaction engines.

Real time. Time in which reporting on events or recording of events is simultaneous with the events. For example, the real time of a satellite is that time in which it simultaneously reports its environment as it encounters it; the real time of a computer is that time during which it is accepting data.

Reentry. The event occurring when a spacecraft or other object comes back into the sensible atmosphere after being rocketed to altitudes above the sensible atmosphere; the action involved in this event.

Reentry window. The area at the limits of the earth's atmosphere through which a spacecraft in a given trajectory can pass to accomplish a successful reentry.

Rendezvous. The event of two or more objects meeting at a preconceived time and place. A rendezvous would be involved, for example, in servicing or resupplying a space station.

Retrorocket. A rocket fitted on or in a spacecraft, satellite, or the like to produce thrust opposed to forward motion.

Rocket. A projectile, pyrotechnic device, or flying vehicle propelled by a rocket engine. A rocket engine.

Rocket engine. A reaction engine that contains within itself, or carries along with itself, all the substances necessary for its operation or for the consumption or combustion of its fuel, not requiring intake of any outside substance and hence capable of operation in outer space. Also called 'rocket motor.'

Rocket propellant. Any agent used for consumption or combustion in a rocket and from which the rocket derives its thrust, such as a fuel, oxidizer, additive, catalyst, or any compound or mixture of these. 'Rocket propellant' is often shortened to 'propellant.'

Roll. The rotational or oscillatory movement of an aircraft or similar body which takes place about a longitudinal axis through the body— called 'roll' for any amount of such rotation.

Rotation. Turning of a body about an axis within the body, as the daily rotation of the earth.

Rudder. A vertically mounted control surface usually attached to the vertical fin, that is hinged to swing to the left or right. The rudder in an airplane controls the tendency of the aircraft to yaw to the left or right. Used properly with the ailerons, it allows smooth turns and other maneuvers. The rudder of a ship or submarine also controls the tendency of seagoing craft to yaw, and is used to steer the ship in any desired direction.

Satellite. An attendant body that revolves about another body, the primary; especially in the solar system, a secondary body or moon, that revolves about a planet. A manmade object that revolves about a spatial body, such as Explorer I orbiting about the earth.

Screaming. A form of combustion instability, especially in a liquid-propellant rocket engine, of relatively high frequency and characterized by a high-pitched noise.

Sensor. The component of an instrument that converts an input signal into a quantity which is measured by another part of the instrument. Also called 'sensing element.'

Shot. An act or instance of firing a rocket, especially from the earth's surface, as 'the shot carried the rocket 200 miles.'

Solar cell. A photovoltaic device that converts sunlight directly into electrical energy.

Solid propellant. Specifically, a rocket propellant in solid form, usually containing both fuel and oxidizer combined or mixed and formed into a monolithic (not powered or granulated) grain.

Solid-propellant rocket engine. A rocket engine using a solid propellant. Such engines consist essentially of a combustion chamber containing the propellant, and a nozzle for the exhaust jet, although they often contain other components, as grids, liners, etc.

Solar wind. A stream of protons constantly moving outward from the sun.

Space. Specifically, the part of the universe lying outside the limits of the earth's atmosphere. More generally, the volume in which all spatial bodies, including the earth, move.

Spacecraft. Devices, manned and unmanned, which are designed to be placed into an orbit about the earth or into a trajectory to another celestial body.

Stage. A propulsion unit of a rocket, especially one unit of a multistage rocket, including its own fuel and tanks.

Stage-and-a-half. A liquid-rocket propulsion unit of which only part falls away from the rocket vehicle during flight, as in the case of booster rockets falling away to leave the sustainer engine to consume remaining fuel.

Stationary orbit. An orbit in which an equatorial satellite revolves about the primary at the same angular rate as the primary rotates on its axis. From the primary, the satellite thus appears to be stationary over a point on the primary.

Sustainer engine. An engine that maintains the velocity of a missile or rocket vehicle, once it has achieved its programmed velocity through use of a booster engine.

Synchronous satellite. An equatorial west-to-east satellite orbiting the earth at an altitude of 22,300 statute miles at which altitude it makes one revolution in 24 hours, synchronous with the earth's rotation.

Telemetry. The science of measuring a quantity or quantities transmitting the measured value to a distant station, and there interpreting, indicating, or recording the quantities measured.

Thrust. The pushing force developed by an aircraft engine or a rocket engine. Specifically, in rocketry, the product of propellant mass flow rate and exhaust velocity relative to the vehicle.

Transfer orbit. In interplanetary travel an elliptical trajectory tangent to the orbits of both the departure planet and the target planet.

Translunar. Of or pertaining to space outside the moon's orbit about the earth.

Van Allen belt, Van Allen radiation belt. (For James A. Van Allen, 1915- .) The zone of high-intensity radiation surrounding the earth beginning at altitudes of approximately 500 miles.

Vernier engine. A rocket engine of small thrust used primarily to obtain a fine adjustment in the velocity and trajectory of a ballistic missile or space vehicle just after the thrust cutoff of the last propulsion engine, and used secondarily to add thrust to a booster or sustainer engine. Also called 'vernier rocket.'

Vertical. The direction in which the force of gravity acts.

Vertical fin. A fixed vertical surface that forms part of the tail. It provides directional stability for the airplane in flight. The rudder is usually hinged to the vertical fin. Vertical and horizontal fins in submarines are utilized along with their hinged surfaces to control the direction and stability of submerged undersea craft.

Weightlessness. A condition in which no acceleration, whether of gravity or other force, can be detected by an observer within the system in question. Any object falling freely in a vacuum is weightless, thus an unaccelerated satellite orbiting the earth is 'weightless' although gravity affects its orbit. Weightlessness can be produced within the atmosphere in aircraft flying a parabolic flight path.

Wing. An airfoil; the lifting surface of an airplane.

Yaw. The later rotational or oscillatory movement of an aircraft, rocket, or the like about a transverse axis. The amount of this movement, i.e., the angle of yaw.

Zero g. Weightlessness.

Bibliography

Bergaust, Erik and Beller, William. *Satellite!* Garden City, New York: Hanover House, 1956.

Bowditch, Nathaniel. *American Practical Navigator.* Washington, D.C.: U.S. Navy Department Hydrographic Office, 1943.

Buchheim, Robert W., et al. *New Space Handbook: Astronautics and Its Applications.* New York: Vintage Books, 1963.

Caidin, Martin. *Let's Go Flying!* New York: E. P. Dutton & Company, Inc., 1961.

House of Representatives, 85th Congress, 2nd Session. *Space Handbook: Astronautics and Its Applications.* Washington, D.C.

House of Representatives, 86th Congress, 1st Session. *The Next Ten Years in Space, 1959-1969.* Washington, D.C.: U.S. Government Printing Office, 1960.

Orman, Leonard M. *Electronic Navigation.* North Hollywood, California: Pan-American Navigation Service, 1950.

Polowe, David. *Navigation for Mariners and Aviators.* New York: Cornell Maritime Press, 1942.

Sparks, James C., Jr., *Gyroscopes.* New York: E. P. Dutton & Company, Inc., 1963.

Weems, Philip V. H. *Air Navigation.* New York: McGraw-Hill Book Company, 1943.

Index